Serena Gray is the author of *The Slag's Almanac* and *Beached on the Shores of Love*. Her work has appeared in *Cosmopolitan* and *Woman's Own*.

Also by Serena Gray

THE SLAG'S ALMANAC
BEACHED ON THE SHORES OF LOVE

LIFE'S
A
BITCH ...
AND THEN YOU DIET

Serena Gray

Futura

A Futura Book

First published in Great Britain in 1991 by Futura Publications,
A Division of Macdonald & Co (Publishers) Ltd
London & Sydney

Typeset in Great Britain by Leaper & Gard Limited
Printed and bound by
BPCC Hazell Books
Aylesbury, Bucks, England
Member of BPCC Ltd.

ISBN 0 7088 4853 2

Futura Publications
A Division of
Macdonald & Co (Publishers) Ltd
Orbit House
1 New Fetter Lane
London EC4A 1AR

A member of Maxwell Macmillan Pergamon Publishing Corporation

'I eat when I'm depressed
and I eat when I'm happy.
When I can't decide
whether I'm tired or hungry
I make the decision while I'm eating.'

Oprah Winfrey

Contents

PART ONE

LIFE'S A BITCH

Introduction

Welcome to the Real World

It is at about the age of twelve that a person first becomes seriously aware that life, though most of the time better than death, is not always exactly a party.

Up until then, our person had been moving along from day to day and year to year in a relatively easy-going way — eating chocolate digestives and watching cartoons — more or less oblivious to the grimmer aspects of tellurian existence. A bad day for her was one on which her favourite television programme was cancelled. A very bad day was one on which her teacher shouted at her in front of the whole class for not doing her homework. Purgatory was not being invited to Emily Anderson's birthday party. Hell was being invited to Emily Anderson's birthday party, turning up in the wrong clothes, discovering that no one else wanted to sit next to her, and then vomiting all over the living room carpet during musical chairs. A tragedy was when her mother made her wear those blue boots to school. A double tragedy was when her mother made her wear those blue boots *and* a thermal vest that showed under her dress.

But then comes that twilight zone between childhood and adulthood, the teenage years, and things begin to change. Hormones start marching through her body. Ideas start steaming through her head. Our person has strolled through the golden days of her youth, thinking of life as a pal, but now she begins to see the world with new eyes. There are bad things out there, all is not sunshine and light. All at once it occurs to her that the reason the stories of her childhood all ended with 'happily ever after' was not because, as she had thought, everything that happened to the heroine and hero past that point was good and wonderful, but because it was so awful that no one wanted to talk about it. Finding out there is no Father Christmas turns out to be the least of our person's problems. Life, she comes to realize, is filled with strife and unhappiness, riddled with misery and suffering, underlined and splattered with heartaches and tears. Life is not a nice, pleasant, considerate friend, there to see that she has a good time. Life is a bitch.

And nor is that all. Life's bad attitude, it turns out, is only the beginning. For now the world begins seeing her with new eyes, too. Our person becomes aware of her body.

When a person is small, her body is just this thing she hangs around in, as reliable and useful as a sheepdog, and treated in much the same way, 'Good Ol' Shep'. Our prepubescent person never paid her body that much attention. She arose in the morning and washed it as though it were a pair of old socks. She put some clothes on it. She put some food in it. She took it out and treated it any old way. Every few days she dunked it in a tub of water and dribbled shampoo in its eyes. Periodically it had its hair cut, its nails clipped and the gunge dug out of its ears, events that were often performed while the body in question was trying to do something else. 'Sit still!' our person's mother would order, yanking her back in the chair. 'Stop fidgeting!' Then mum would fluff out the fringe so that it looked more or less even. 'Well,' she would sigh, 'I guess that's good enough.' 'Of course it is,' our person would cry, and hurry outside to play.

She was an innocent, our person. She didn't yet know that you can't just take your body out into the cold light of day without hours of anxiety and preparation beforehand. She didn't yet know that soap is bad for her skin and that she shouldn't be caught dead in the colour blue. She was still unaware of her eyebrows. It never once dawned on her that every person she passed on the street was looking at her body and thinking: 'Too skinny', 'Too fat', 'Good grief, those knees!' It hadn't occurred to her that her body was in competition with every other female body on the planet, and that 99 per cent of the time her body was going to lose. No one had told her yet about diet cola, chubettes, mature figures, Weight Watchers, cellulite, or killer thighs. Her mother, besides skirting around the issues of orgasms, oral sex and labour pain, had neglected to give her the lowdown on depilatory creams, water retention, stretch marks and facial hair. She didn't know about her bum.

But that all goes the way of the recorder lessons and the stuffed animal collection when she reaches twelve. Little Jacky Paper doesn't go back to see Puff the Magic Dragon, and Susanna Flower, the most popular girl in her class, starts wearing a bra. Our person, hitherto interested in a wide range of subjects from football to cat's cradle to intergalactic travel, suddenly becomes obsessed with the human form. Will she ever have one? Will it be a good one? Are nipples that go in better than nipples that go out? What about belly buttons? Do her thighs bulge when she wears jeans? She and her friends used to be able to walk down the street, rattling off multiplication tables and singing the week's Top Ten to one another between jokes about willies, but suddenly all they can think about is female bodies. Previously just ordinary kids with a laissez-faire attitude towards other people's looks, they become judgmental. 'She's got a good figure,' they sigh sagely. They shake their heads, 'Oh, poor Kirstie, she should never wear her hair up. She looks like Mr Spock in drag.' 'Ooooh,' they squawk, 'look at that fat old cow in the mini skirt, she must be thirty if she's a day!' They collapse together at the bus stop, convulsed with the giggles. 'My God!' they shriek, 'Look at how close together her eyes are! Did you see that nose?!'

Our person starts looking in the mirror. Of course, she used to look in the mirror before, to see if there was any chocolate on her mouth, or if her Aunt Sally had left a lipstick imprint on her cheek, but now she is serious about looking in the mirror. She is looking for spots. She is looking for cracks in her skin. She is looking for pores. She is checking the size of her eyebrows, the length of her lashes, the hollowness of her cheeks. She measures her eyes. She measures her teeth. She measures the distance between her ears and her nose. She measures her nose. At night, she starts taping up her chin and taping down her hair. She decides, as millions of women have decided before her, that certain death by carcinogens is better than being mousey brown.

She remembers that there's a full-length mirror in her mother's room. Only a few days ago, this full-length mirror had seemed a laughable extravagance to her. After all, you can see your feet, you can see your skirt, you know what your sweatshirt looks like, who could possibly need a six-foot sheet of glass? But now she understands who needs it. She needs it. How else can she get any perspective on her calves? How else can she determine whether or not that new pink dress makes her look like a marshmallow? It is while she is standing in front of this mirror that our person first notices that her bum is too big (or that her thighs wobble, or that her tummy is not board-like, or that, for some perverted reason, God made her without a waist). The world goes silent. Dark and silent. A cold, dank feeling creeps up our person's spine. Bile stings the back of her throat. Where there used to be balloons and music, laughter and gaiety, international arms talks and debt crises, circuses and fun fairs, endangered species and water pollution, ice cream sundaes and dancing in the streets, there is now only a big, empty, black-and-white room, a harsh, megawatt spotlight, and, beneath that spotlight, our person and her fat bum. Lot looking back and seeing his wife turned to salt had nothing on our person as she stares at her reflection. She moves and it quivers. She shakes and the air rumbles. Oh, what a fool she's been! All these years she's been sitting on it, and walking around with it, and putting it in shorts and jeans and pretty skirts, and all along it's been getting ready to betray her, to look as though it leaves rooms five minutes after she does. What a wally! How can she have learned the names of all the Tudor kings and the nine-times multiplication table, and not have known about this? Where late the sweet birds sang is now heard only the voice of Jane Fonda saying sharply, 'Remember, discipline is liberation!'

Our person goes to her father.

'Father' she says, 'do you think I'm fat?'

Her father looks up from the copy of the *Sun* he is reading, tucked inside *The Times*. 'Fat?' says her father 'You? Of course you're not fat, you're my baby.' He pinches her cheek.

Our person eyes her father with a new scepticism born of the sudden realization that women like Cher do not have pinchable cheeks but caverns where hands disappear. 'Are you sure?' she asks.

'Positive,' says her father. 'And anyway, pet, I love you just the way you are.'

For the first time in her life, our person does not find this fact comforting.

Our person goes to her mother.

'Mother,' she says, 'do you think I'm fat?'

Being her mother, her mother keeps her eyes on the pieces of metal she's welding together and says, 'No, darling, of course I don't.'

A warm bubble of hope rises in our person. Maybe it's not as bad as she thought.

'After all,' continues her mother, not even blinking as the sparks fly, 'boys like girls with a little meat on their bones.'

The bubble bursts. It's worse than our person thought.

Our person goes to her best friend.

'Do you think I should have my bum cut off?' she asks.

Her best friend, just coming to grips with her own traumatic discovery about her thighs, is sympathetic. 'Hold on!' she cries. 'There's something you can do that's a lot less drastic than that.'

'Really?' asks our person.

'Really,' says her friend. 'You won't believe it. It'll solve everything.

'Well, what is it?' cries our person excitedly. 'Is it a pill?'

Her friend shakes her head. 'Uh uh.'

'Is it a minor operation?'

Her friend shakes her head. 'No.'

'Is it a magic spell?'

Her friend's headshake is emphatic. 'My sister told me about it. It's this wonderful new thing. It's incredible. In two days you have the body of an haute couture model.'

'You're kidding!' exclaims our person. 'Two days?!'

Her best friend, who is not kidding, but who might as well be, says, 'No! Cross my heart and hope to die.'

'And it works? It truly works?'

'Absolutely. Guaranteed.'

'Why, this is terrific!' says our person. 'This is tremendous! This is the answer to my prayers! What is this thing?'

Her best friend smiles, just the way she smiled when she was dishing out the information on sexual intercourse. 'A diet!'

You're smiling, too, aren't you? You're thinking, there it goes, the end of innocence. Imagine not knowing what a diet is! Imagine not being on a first-name basis with calories, carbohydrates, fats and fibres! Imagine thinking of food by its proper names (steak and chips, spaghetti with clam sauce, spinach and mushroom salad with blue cheese dressing and portions of onion rings and garlic bread, chocolate fudge cake with chocolate ice cream and chocolate sauce) instead of as the number of days you'll have to go without eating to burn it off (six, two, a week and a half, the rest of your life). Imagine being able to consume a bacon and egg sandwich without having to apologize to your hips first or go to confession afterwards!

But our person hasn't lost all of her innocence yet, of course. Because she still doesn't know. She still doesn't know that she will never again, for as long as she lives, be able to eat a cheeseburger and a family bag of beef and onion crisps with the same mood of gay abandon as she did in her youth. She doesn't yet really understand that it is not the ignorant or the greedy, the multinationals or the media manipulators, the unscrupulous politicians or the drugs traffickers that are her enemy — it is food. That every chicken wing, chocolate bar and tablespoon of thousand island dressing is out to get her. That when she reaches for the packet of custard creams, that packet is grinning at her and saying, 'Go on, sister, make my day!' It hasn't even occurred to her to ask that all-important question: 'Just how long am I going to be on this diet for?'

It certainly hasn't occurred to her that the answer to that question is: 'Forever.'

1.

Come Back, Nancy Reagan, All is Forgiven

Thin Is a Feminine Issue

Just as there is a tradition in America of strong Presidents — fearless, rugged men whose boldness, brashness and vision have shaped the world as we know it — so there is a tradition of strong First Ladies. No Dennis Thatchers, these, content to simply shuffle around in the background, knocking back the gin and arranging the place settings. Oh no. We are speaking here of women who have contributed as much — if not more — to modern culture as the men whose names grace high schools and airports and sports centres all over the United States.

'You mean like Eleanor Roosevelt?' I hear you ask.

Well, sort of like Eleanor Roosevelt. But not exactly. Eleanor Roosevelt, did, it is true, have many fine qualities — intelligence, dignity, integrity, honesty, tireless energy and a willingness to champion unpopular causes — and no one could deny the importance of the work she did for the United Nations. But Eleanor Roosevelt wasn't exactly the sort of woman our society encourages our girls to model themselves after, was she? She was feminine only when compared to a Sherman tank. She was graceful only when put up against a tractor. No one would have asked Eleanor Roosevelt to model bikinis. No man would have chased her down the street to hand her a bouquet of flowers. Eleanor Roosevelt, friend of a suffering humanity that she may have been, bore an unfortunate physical resemblance to a bulldog. Eleanor Roosevelt had a weight problem.

'Oh, I get it. You mean First Ladies who are all women that we, as ordinary people, can look up to and admire. Whose behaviour and ideals we should try to emulate. Whose work has made a lasting contribution to our world.'

Exactly. We are talking real women here.

Betty Ford and the clinic that bears her name. Jackie Kennedy and the concept of continuous shopping. Nancy Reagan and what some regard as the most profound and significant statement to be made during her husband's presidency: 'A woman can never be too thin.'

Think about it. A woman can never be too thin.

Some people, people who were used to scoffing at anything said by Nancy Reagan, scoffed. 'Pfft,' they said. 'What a stupid thing to say. What would you expect from a woman who is married to a man who believes that trees cause air pollution?' The fact of the matter is, however, that while women in certain Third World countries might quibble with Mrs Reagan's analysis, likening it to a rather famous if ill-advised remark about cake, millions of Western women agree with the former First Lady. And agree vociferously. A girl can never be too thin. She can be too tall, she can be too short, she can be too solid, she can be too flat or too busty, she can talk too much or be too quiet, but she can't be too thin. To suggest that a woman can be too thin, millions believe, is the equivalent of saying that snow can be too white or that there's too much sand in Jamaica.

'Wait a minute,' you say. 'Didn't Susie Orbach say that fat is a feminist issue?'

'Susie who?' comes the reply. 'She's probably as big as a house,' the reply continues. 'I wouldn't be surprised if she tried liposuction and it failed. I bet she's bitter. I bet she's never been out on a date. Fat is a feminist issue indeed.'

Bodyweight, Hair Colour, Skin Condition and You

Nonetheless, it is true that until Nancy Reagan went public about the Western attitude to female body size a certain amount of confusion did still exist. It was possible for a person to get her signals crossed.

You went to the cinema and all the women — all the ones anyone in her right mind would want to identify with, that is, the ones who got to kiss Sean Connery before he shot them or swing over a pit of vipers clinging to Harrison Ford — all these women were not only stunningly beautiful, they were so thin that if it weren't biologically impossible, you would have assumed that the reason they looked as though they had no stomachs was because they didn't and therefore never ate anything. Wow, you thought, I suppose women who aren't gorgeous and skinny kill themselves or stay indoors.

You meandered through the local newsagents. You flipped through a few magazines. All the women in the magazines — except for the woman with the thirteen handicapped foster children who had received a special Mother of the Year Award from the Queen — were flawlessly beautiful and thin as a shadow. No hair grew on their legs or on the insides of their twiglike thighs. Their skin didn't have pores. Their love didn't have handles. These women all wore beautiful clothes (or didn't wear clothes beautifully), and were laughing and fooling around with handsome young men. These women were happy and having a good time. Life liked them. Life showered them with gifts. They were popular and loved. Life wasn't a bitch to them. Life was their best friend. You flipped back to the article on the Mother of the Year. She claimed to be happy and fulfilled. Things weren't always easy, times were often hard, but she had a sense of accomplishment. You took another peek at the advertisement on the tropical island. Sixteen men — all of whom made Michael Douglas look average — were hanging from palm trees or kneeling in the snow-white sand, offering the size-eight woman in the silver sarong a fabulous piece of jewellery. The young woman in the silver sarong was laughing her heart out. The Mother of the Year was smiling determinedly as she tried to keep a small child from gouging out her eye with a spoon. A thought occurred to you. The Mother of the Year, to be honest, didn't have much going for her except her heart of gold. If you were going to be really honest, she was pudgy and dowdy and looked like a Cabbage Patch Doll that had grown up. No heartbreakingly handsome man was going to want to splash water on her or shower her with jewels. Well, you thought, I suppose women who aren't attractive can't expect to have normal lives with full social calendars and great sex. I guess they have to settle for helping crippled children to take three steps across the lawn.

You wandered through the local bookshop. No stirring sagas about plain-looking women with limp hair and thick thighs there. No fat heroines. No true love for anyone with a full figure and crooked teeth. No romance or adventure for the girl with a big bum and bad skin. Forget about fiction, you thought, I'll see if there are any good books on transcendental meditation or sheep shearing in the non-fiction section. No, not a one. Instead, there are fifty different diet books, fifteen different exercise books, several hundred guides to skin care, hair care and

cosmetic surgery, and forty-three manuals on men.
You started leafing through a book that guaranteed
you thinner thighs, narrower hips and a flatter bum.
The thighs on the women in the before picture
looked a lot like yours. You flipped through the book
describing a diet used by some of the most beautiful
and sexy women in Hollywood. It guaranteed that
you would lose ten pounds in the first week — and
have fun doing it. Ten pounds? In one week? Without
having your jaw welded or being locked in a cell in
the middle of the Antarctic? Maybe you should try it.
After all, you stuck to your last diet for two weeks
and all you lost was fourteen days. You flicked
through the book describing another diet used by
another group of beautiful and sexy Hollywood stars.
This one guaranteed a weight loss of only eight
pounds in the first week, but you didn't have to cut
out alcohol and you weren't limited to pink grapefruit
and crispbread. Maybe you should try this one too.
Well, you thought, as you paid for your half a dozen
books, I suppose being skinny and pretty is much
more important than achieving nirvana any day.

You were sitting in front of the television, watching
adverts one night. You'd already sat through dozens
of adverts for everything from chocolates to compact
cars, and in every one the key figure was an
amazingly attractive young woman who had never
had to lie on the floor while someone else zipped up
her jeans. Well, you thought, I suppose ordinary-
looking women with imperfect bodies never get taken
out, are never telephoned or visited by masked men
in the middle of the night, never drive nice cars or
drink coffee or get to launder any man's shirts. And
then came an ad for a popular soft drink. An immacu-
lately beautiful and sylph-like young woman knocks
on the door of the apartment across the hall from

hers and asks to borrow a can of cola. Diet cola. The young man whom she asks, barely able to speak in the presence of such slimline splendour, dashes inside to get a can of cola. Only he doesn't have any cola. Not diet cola. So he clambers out the window. It is raining. He races down the fire escape. It isn't just raining, it's biblical justice. He battles his way through a street gang, a pack of wild dogs, two car chases and a crowd scene from *Julius Caesar* to buy her a can of cola. When he finally gets back home and hands it to her, she smiles, showing all of her perfect teeth and her remarkable bone structure, and says, 'Thank you. I hope I didn't put you to any trouble.' Panting slightly and dripping water all over the carpet, he says, 'No, no, no trouble.' You laughed because you suddenly remembered the time you (plain and a size twelve-and-a-half when you're not retaining water) had the flu in Sri Lanka and sent the man you were travelling with out for a bottle of Coke to save your life. You remembered that he came back twelve hours later, without the Coke, and responded to your frail query about your drink with a curt, 'Do you think I have nothing to do but wait on you?' You experienced a flash of understanding. Women who are not physically perfect can't expect much from anyone — not from men, that's for sure, and certainly not from life.

Who's Afraid of Nancy Reagan?

But then what happened? You walked outside and there, in broad daylight, for all the world to see, were hundreds, even thousands, maybe millions, of women whose eyes weren't limpid pools, whose skin was composed of trillions of eccentric, temperamental little cells and not alabaster, whose noses weren't as straight as rulers, whose hair didn't shine or bounce or smell like a forest stream. There, riding buses and driving cars and hailing taxis, were average-looking women with imperfect faces and lumpy bodies. Women who clearly consumed more than eight hundred calories a day and knew what it felt like to eat thirty-six bourbon creams in one sitting. Women who dressed in the dark. Women who washed their faces and put on their make-up by the light of a 40-watt bulb. Many of these women were wearing wedding rings. Many of these women were pushing prams, or holding the hand of a perfectly decent-looking man, or carrying attaché cases or artist port-folios. They didn't look as though they were unused to natural light. They didn't look as though their lives had been ruined by dull brown hair, fat cheeks, or stubby ankles. They were smiling — not with teeth that Farrah Fawcett would envy, maybe, but smiling just the same. They looked busy. They looked happy. They looked like they had jobs and friends and homes and love lives and interesting hobbies.

'Hey, hang on a minute,' you said to yourself, 'a woman doesn't have to look like a model to have a good life. It's all right to be a normal size. It's okay to be a regular sort of weight. It isn't a crime to eat. Hips aren't illegal. Women with thighs aren't slapped in jail. Girls who have mid-riff bulge or double-chins can still be loved.' Boom Shiva! You thought you might just treat yourself to a chocolate bar in cele-bration. You even considered eating lunch. But then, just as you were about to order a sandwich *with* bread and a helping of potato salad, the voice of Nancy Reagan was heard throughout the world.

'A woman can never be too thin,' boomed Nancy Reagan. 'NEVER!'

All eyes turned to you. You'd just taken your first

gigantic bite of fatty meat, starch, pickle and mustard (a bite worth at least 1,500 calories and two weeks of guilt).

'Did you hear me?' Nancy Reagan roared. 'NOT EVER!' You put down your sandwich and rushed home to glue your lips together.

My friend Jane Forbes-Smythe called me up the minute she heard the news. 'You see, Serena?' she said in that rather annoying way she has when she feels she's been proven right. 'What did I tell you?'

I hastily shoved the box of cheese biscuits back into the cupboard. 'Who'd listen to a woman who dresses like an airline hostess for a company operating from Guernsey?' I asked defensively.

'What was that?' asked Jane. 'Were you just going to *eat* something?'

Jane is the only person I know who can smell food through walls, over rivers and down telephone lines. 'Uh uh,' I exaggerated slightly. 'I was just getting a low-calorie tea bag out of the tin.'

'I bet,' said Jane, sniffing. 'I'm sure I smell cheese flavouring.' She paused theatrically. 'You know what your trouble is, Serena?' asked Jane. 'I mean besides your hips.'

'My elbows?'

'No, your trouble is that you know Nancy Reagan is right, but you don't want to admit it. You just can't face the fact that a diet isn't just a passing phase, it's a way of life.'

'I thought it was diamonds that were forever,' I ventured.

'Not if you're not on a diet they're not,' countered Jane.

Jane is right when she says that I am reluctant to face the fact of a lifetime spent worrying about the diameter of your upper arms. And nor — despite Mrs Reagan, Ms Forbes-Smythe, and what might be taken as considerable evidence to the contrary (the fact that more than 50 per cent of the female population is on a diet at any given time) — am I the only person on this planet who finds the concept of the lifetime diet, like the concept of a nuclear holocaust, a little unsettling and hard to take.

'Oh, come on,' say the naturally slender or the naturally stubborn or the unashamedly plump. 'You must be joking.' 'You can't be serious,' say those who have never been on a diet in their lives, those who would rather live in a bat cave than miss a meal. 'A lifetime diet? No one goes on a diet for more than a month or two unless they're lost in the Amazon and living on ants.'

These people are unaware that dieting is a billion-pound industry. These people don't worry about their hips twenty-four hours a day. They don't become distraught when they think of their thighs. They don't go into a state of shock every time they catch a glimpse of themselves in a full-length mirror. They may even believe that the occasional chocolate soufflé or onion bhaji is worth a few extra pounds of body weight, what the hell. They certainly don't jump in fright every time someone offers them a biscuit. They couldn't tell you how many calories there are in a tuna sandwich, sans crust and celery, if their lives depended on it. The hearts of these people don't race every time they see an advertisement for something — anything — that will thin their thighs or trim their tummies or reduce their knees. They don't talk to their weighing scales. Their weighing scales don't talk back to them. They don't read every new magazine article that promises to tell them how to get in shape for the summer, how to get in shape for the autumn, how to get in shape after Christmas, how to get in shape for the spring, how to lose fifteen pounds in three short, effortless days, how to look slimmer in a day-and-a-half. Perhaps these people even had their heads in the fridge on the day that Nancy Reagan made her announcement. Perhaps the rustle of crips packets covered up the sound of millions of Western women cheering in agreement, 'Atta girl, Nance! You tell 'em! Never too thin!!'

'Wait a minute, wait a minute,' they say. 'If you believe that a woman can never be too thin, then it follows that you must also believe that all women are overweight.'

Um, I think that's a fair assessment.

Life, after all, is quite a bitch.

2.

Life and You: A Short Quiz

Do you agree with Mrs Reagan? Or do you disagree? If you agree, do you think that you agree because your attitude towards life and your body's role in it is clear and balanced? If you disagree, do you think that you disagree because your attitude toward the world around you and your physical self is unpressured by the propaganda and prejudice of a society that still thinks of women as objects? Or are you confused? Muddled? Do you not really know either what you think or why? Here's a short quiz to help you find out what your attitude toward life and your own corporeal presence really is.

Answer true or false to the following clear, unambiguous statements. No maybes are allowed. No conditional clauses are permitted. Consultation with friends or family members is out. We want spontaneous reactions here. We want just true or false.

Beauty is Only Skin Deep

1. True. For heaven's sake, everybody knows that. What you look like isn't important. It's what sort of person you are inside that counts. After all, everyone but Cher and Joan Collins gets old. Your hair goes grey, your skin sags, your face drops. That's life. But if you're a well-rounded person with a good personality and a strong character who hasn't spent the last twenty

years trying to keep the body of a sixteen-year-old, it won't matter. You'll have lots of friends and interests. Your life will get better and better. Your body may get old but your heart will remain young. The true beauty that comes with experience and wisdom will shine through. Of course, that doesn't mean that a woman shouldn't always look her best or should let herself go. Inner beauty in a size eight body and firm thighs is better than inner beauty in a body that weighs in at ten stone and whose eyes are too close together.

2. False. If beauty is only skin deep, why are more men attracted to women who look like Playboy Bunnies than they are to women who look like real rabbits? Why are most of the successful, powerful, attractive, wealthy, and famous men in the world married to blondes with eighteen-inch waists who spend more on clothes and make-up than the entire national debt of Guatemala? Why would even a man as obviously sensitive and intelligent as Bruce Springsteen marry a module? I'll tell you why. Because nobody really believes that beauty is only skin deep. Everybody believes that if you look beautiful and sexy, you are beautiful and sexy. A man doesn't want to think that when he walks out of the party or turns up to the Academy Awards with his wife or girlfriend everybody's going to be nudging each other and saying, 'Wow, I bet she's a great conversationalist,' or 'I bet that lady's one hell of a cook!' They want to think that all the men have hard-ons and are whispering to each other, 'Mama mia, look at those legs!' You don't think it's an accident, do

you, that it was Cyrano who had the big nose and not Roxanne? You don't think kids would still be reading *Beauty and the Beast* if the beast had been a woman and Beauty could have been played by Matt Dillon?

3. True twice. It's true that beauty is only skin deep. But it's also true that, on the whole, people exercise their eyes a lot more than they exercise their cerebrums. Nobody is half as interested in your brilliance when it comes to analyzing political situations, as they are in the straightness of your teeth and the size of your trousers. You may be able to catch the attention of the man you meet at the astro-physicist's convention with your ability to work out the square root of eighteen-digit numbers in your head, but you can bet your best mini-skirt that if you're built like a postbox he'll be asking the waitress in the coffee shop (who is built like Jamie Lee Curtis and counts on her fingers) for her phone number, not you.

Dieting Makes you Fat

1. Well, that can't be true, can it? False. Dieting doesn't make you fat. How can eating pineapple for a month possibly make you fat? By the end of the second week you're so sick of the stuff you're not eating anything anyway. And remember the seaweed and kumquat diet? You'd be amazed how little 'all the seaweed and kumquats you can eat' is. So, no, dieting doesn't make you fat. The funny thing is though, that dieting doesn't always exactly make you thin.

Even if you weigh out every eight ounces of cereal and measure every three fluid ounces of skimmed milk precisely and never cheat when it comes to eating your grapefruit without sugar (which, if you ask me, is the gastronomic equivalent of wearing your trainers without socks to play hockey on a hot day), sometimes it can happen that every morning you get on the scales and every morning the scales say the same depressing thing they said the morning before, which is not what you wanted them to say. I don't know why this is. I think it must be what they call a plateau.

2. False, false, false. Who ever heard of anything so stupid? Dieting doesn't make you fat. Dieting makes you thin. And if you can learn to cut out things like bread and pasta and potatoes altogether, dieting won't make you just thin, it'll make you skinny. Think of that! Dieting makes you beautiful and desirable. Nobody's saying that dieting is easy. It is not easy. It is hard work. It takes discipline and willpower. It takes self-control. You have to be strong. And sometimes, of course, a person might slip. You might finish your salad of lettuce, cucumber and two ounces of cottage cheese with a dressing made out of lemon juice and a little pepper, and all of a sudden you find yourself standing in front of the fridge, eating cold macaroni cheese and digging the pickled onions out of the bottom of the jar with your fingers, but you can't let something like that ruin your day. And if you put a few extra hours into your aerobics that week you might just work most of it off.

3. True. You can only feed yourself on carrot sticks and boiled chicken — no butter, no gravy — for so long and then whoopee! your body rebels. Unless you seal off your nostrils, you're likely to find yourself walking past a bakery — a bakery that a normal person who eats normal meals could pass without a second glance — and instead of passing you find the aroma of freshly baked buns makes you stop by the door for a second, and the next thing you know you're yanked inside by a force that is greater even than your abject terror of powdered sugar. Now a normal person who had had her breakfast and her lunch might catch a whiff of those jam doughnuts and think, yes, I'm going to get myself one of those. And get herself one of those is exactly what she'd do. One. But you, not having had a real meal since the night before you started on this month's diet, buy a dozen. You buy a dozen and eat the first two before you're even out of the shop. You kill off the next eight by the end of the road. The last two you swallow whole while you're waiting for the traffic lights to change. You feel so guilty about all this that you stop at the next sweet shop you come to and buy three chocolate bars, two cans of diet cola and six small bags of crisps (they don't have any large ones). By the time you reach home, crumbs scattered behind you like a trail, chocolate all over your shirt and your pockets stuffed with empty wrappers, you feel so: a) guilty; b) fat; c) disgusted with yourself; and d) hungry, that you eat an entire box of cereal (two weeks' worth of measured breakfasts) while standing in the pantry with your

coat still on. How, under those circumstances, could dieting ever make you anything but fat?

The Nicest Thing Anyone Can Ever Say to You Is: 'Why Fiona, You've Lost Weight!'

1. True. In context, of course. I mean, you wouldn't want to be explaining your new promotion and have someone suddenly interrupt you to ask if you're three pounds lighter. Well, actually, I suppose you wouldn't really mind, would you? If they interrupted to say, 'Excuse me, Fiona, but isn't your bum a little more like a pumpkin than it was a few weeks ago?' you'd be rather pissed off. You'd probably cry or throw something at them. But if they cut in to tell you that you're looking better, well, that's all right then. Although I can imagine one or two instances where it wouldn't be appreciated. When you're waiting to hear that your kisses turn his solar plexus to lava or why he's sixteen hours late for your date, for instance. But, nine-and-a-half times out of ten, it's true.

2. True. Absolutely and always true. There is no possible situation this side of heaven in which a person wouldn't be thrilled beyond belief to be told that she's lost weight. It's always a compliment, isn't it? In fact I suppose you could say that it's the ultimate compliment. I mean, it's nice if someone says, 'Well, Fiona, that was the best moussaka I've ever eaten,' or 'I thought your book on the history of Christianity was one of the most intelligent and thorough pieces of scholarship I've ever read,' but it's not half as

wonderful as someone coming up to you on the street and saying, 'Do you look thin!' Anyway, people don't make half the fuss about your history of Christianity that they'll make if you can wear a lycra dance suit and not look like a German sausage. Even if you win the Pulitzer Prize or something, the most you're going to get is a, 'Yes, I saw you got that prize, congratulations. I must read your book some time,' and then it'll never be mentioned again. But lose three stone and no one will ever shut up about it.

3. False. And I'm surprised you have to ask. With all the scope available these days for personal growth and fulfilment, all the opportunities for achievement and self-expression, the idea that your highest goal in life is to have someone come up to you at a party and say, 'Fiona, aren't your thighs an inch-and-a-half smaller?' seems just a wee bit ridiculous to me. I would much prefer that people complimented me on something I'd really done, some contribution I'd made to the wellbeing or the happiness of the planet, no matter how small, than on the fact that I can wear cycling shorts in public without causing major fits of hysteria. Yes, of course I'm telling the truth.

The Worst Thing Anyone Could Ever Say to You Is: 'Er, Fiona, Have We Put on a Little Weight?'

1. True, under normal circumstances. I know, I know, we're not supposed to make qualifying statements, and I'm sorry, I really am, but I

don't think it's my fault. It's these questions. They're not unambiguous at all, if you ask me. Anyway, I think the answer to this one is True, but that's under normal conditions, if you know what I mean. I mean, obviously, there are worse things you can be told. You could be told that you have six months to live. Or you could be told that the planet's about to go up like a Roman candle. Or you could be told that your boyfriend's just run off with your best friend and they took your car and your stereo with them. Those things are out-of-the-ordinary bad. But on an ordinary day when you're worrying about the usual things like your bank manager and your credit card limit and why the windscreen wipers won't start, being told that you're looking more and more like Miss Piggy is about the worst thing you could hope to hear. Or hope not to hear, to be more accurate. To be honest, I would rather miss three buses, have to wait an hour-and-a-half for a train with a group of drunken football supporters, be fired for being late to work, and discover when I finally got back home that the video had been stolen, than have my best friend steel herself on a bottle of vodka and then put her arm around me and say, 'Fiona, love, have you been hitting the tortilla chips again?'

2. Oh true, true, true. In 1988 I broke up with Harold Charterhouse, the nicest and kindest heart surgeon a girl could ever meet, because of an unfortunate remark he made about my hips. We were in this Italian restaurant. Harold had just ordered fried clams and the stuffed auber-gine. The waiter turned to me and said, 'And for

the lady?' I knew for certain that Harold was going to propose before we got to dessert, so I wanted to order something that would go well with champagne. 'I'll have the fettuccine with cream sauce and artichokes,' I said. Harold had this laugh that sounded a bit like water trying to get through a broken hosepipe. Harold went glubglubglubswoosh. 'Darling,' said Harold, not even bothering to lower his voice so the waiter and the other diners couldn't hear him. 'Darling, why bother eating it? Why not just put it straight onto your hips?' I cracked a few bread-sticks over his head and left the trattoria in floods of tears. Harold tried to apologise. He followed me all the way home, saying over and over, 'For heaven's sake, love, I was only joking. I only said it because you're always going on about your hips so much. I love your hips. As far as I'm concerned, the more of them there are, the better.' But I could never marry him after that, could I? I mean, once we were married he'd see me without my make-up. He'd see me when I was sleeping and he'd have the opportunity to really study those little craters in my thighs and those things at the backs of my knees. It was too risky.

And that's not the worst scenario I can think of. What if you were an actress, say, or a screenwriter or something like that. And you're at the Academy Awards, right? You've just won an Oscar. Maybe you wrote, directed and starred in this film and you've just won an Oscar for Best Everything. The crowd's going berserk. Everybody at your table's patting you on the back as you get to your feet. People reach out to touch you as you walk past them to get to the stage. You're thinking about what you're going to say. After you thank your parents and your grandparents and the Cossacks whose policy of blood and terror forced your great-grandparents to leave Russia, you're going to say that this is the happiest day of your life. That this is the best thing that ever happened to you. That if you died now you'd be smiling. You climb up those few steps and walk to the podium. And just as Bruce Willis is handing you your award you hear someone right in the front of the stage turn to their companion and say, 'My God, she's put on weight, hasn't she? Remember when she was so slim?' And that's it, isn't it? You've got two choices. You either mumble something about how proud you are and hope they think you're crying from joy. Or you rush from the podium, through the hall, out the door and in front of the first bus that comes along. You tell me what anyone could say to you that's more awful than that.

3. False. I can think of about 4,355,000 things that are worse than discovering that, when you're not around, your family and friends talk among themselves about how someone should kindly tell you never to wear a bathing suit in public. I'd rather be a few pounds overweight than boring or shallow or self-centred. Yes, I would. Yes, I really mean that.

Fat is a Feminist Issue

1. Am I allowed to answer 'Sort of' here? I mean, I do appreciate that you see a lot more thin,

beautiful women with fat, ugly men than you see devastatingly handsome men built like Greek gods with women with average looks and the body shape of a teddy bear. And I do agree that if you do see a hunky guy with a plain woman with a liking for deep-pan pizzas with extra cheese and anchovies, the first question you ask yourself is usually, 'Good grief, what can he possibly see in her?' So I suppose in that sense the feminists have a point. On the other hand, though, that's just the way things are, isn't it? I mean, women are supposed to be attractive. They're not supposed to let themselves go. A woman's looks have always been her greatest asset. That's a historical fact. You can't really argue with history, can you?

2. False. Fat is about being ugly and unattractive to men, that's what being fat is about. It's about looking like a pin cushion instead of a wood nymph. It's about not being able to wear a bikini without making everybody throw up. Because a lot of feminists don't exactly have the looks or the bodies that drive men wild, rightaway everybody starts banging on about fat being a feminist issue. What rubbish! Having a tummy like a beach ball is not a political statement, for Pete's sake, it's just a turn-off. Not being asked out on a date for twelve years running doesn't mean you're an original thinker. What it probably means is that you get through six packets of biscuits and a half a litre of ice cream every Friday night because you're lonely and unloved. Let's face it, feminists don't look like that because they're feminists. They're feminists because they look like that. I mean, maybe they

don't shave their legs or spend half their salaries on cosmetics, beauty treatments at the health spa, and having their roots done as a matter of principle (you know, because men don't, so they don't see why they should), but being dumpy and having a big nose isn't a matter of principle. It's a combination of too many carbohydrates and bad luck. What do you think when you see some woman who looks like a panda in a tailored suit walking down the street? Do you think, wow, I bet she's a leading feminist thinker? No, you think, my God, somebody should tell her to wear full skirts that camouflage those hips. When you see a bloke who looks like Daley Thompson married to some mousy woman who takes a larger size of jeans than he does, you don't think, she must be brilliant, kind and a world-class wit. You think, I bet she got pregnant so he'd have to marry her.

3. True, true, a thousand times true. Have you ever seen that television advert for a very popular brand of cereal? The first thing you see is a woman in a tight white bathing suit diving into a pool. This woman has a perfect female body in the sense that she doesn't have a female body. No hips. No stomach. No thighs. Breasts that are definitely breasts but not to the point of being intrusive. The slogan is: You can have a breakfast like mine. Anyone seeing that advert knows that what it is really saying is: You can have a body like mine. And when you watch this commercial you automatically find yourself sighing at the first sight of that trim figure with the legs that go up to her armpits and the

stomach that has never had to be sucked in to get the zip done up. You think, I want a body like hers. Then people would admire me. Then men would lust after me. Then I wouldn't have to wear a swimsuit with a skirt. You think, if I had a body like that I would feel secure in myself and confident. I would be beautiful. I would be successful and happy and spend all my time swimming in a private pool in California. But what do other female images used in advertisements and films and television programmes make you think? The dopey next-door neighbour who looks like a turkey; the bossy mother or mother-in-law who looks like a turkey; the nosey, jealous wife who looks like a turkey? They make you think: ugh. They make you think: old. They make you think: ugly. They make you think: failure. They make you think: I'd rather be in traction for the rest of my life than be like that. Every day of our lives, we are bombarded with images of the woman we should strive to be. The heroines in our movies are never short and dumpy and the owners of funny noses. They are always beautiful. They are always slender. Sometimes they have best friends who have more in common with Lassie than Kelly McGillis, but that is usually for comic relief, and to make the leading lady look even better. The heroines in our best-selling novels are not overweight, built like flying buttresses and crowned with thin, lank hair. They are willowy, or willowy but voluptuous, and so gorgeous that they can't walk into a room without causing every man present to forget what he was saying and every penis in the room to rise in salute. When they walk down the street, with their tousled manes blowing in the breeze, traffic stops, waiters pour pitchers of water into the laps of sophisticated men who are too enchanted by the vision of loveliness walking past the window to notice. So of course, fat is a feminist issue. The pressure on women to be slim, the message that is reinforced time and time again that thin is beautiful and skinny is sexy and that women who are attractive get everything — good lives, great times, romance and unending love — and the fact that the same message is not given to men and that a man's sexuality and success as a person are not dependent on whether or not his stomach rises over the waist of his bikini, mean that fat is not only a feminist issue, it means that fat, and our attitude to it, is one of the most important issues of our society and culture.

Scoring

Give yourself two points for every 1, three points for every 2, and one point for every 3.

If you scored five points you and life get along just fine. You like it and it likes you. Your attitude towards it is not based on the flimsy and the superficial but on concrete things. Not for one nanosecond are you fooled by the cultural propaganda that makes women believe that their happiness and personal fulfilment depends on what size stretchpants they wear. On the other hand, as Jane Forbes-Smythe has pointed out, it probably also means that you'll never get a date with Michael Douglas. Or even King Kong for that matter. Jane also thinks that you sound a little bitter. She for one wouldn't want your frown lines. She wonders how bad your stretchmarks are. She bets you've got the complexion of an old gym sock and have never been on an exercise bike in your life — and that it shows. She says it's unusual in this day and age to meet anyone who's never even thought of sealing the refrigerator with Super Glue, but she reckons you're that person.

If you scored over five but no more than ten, your intelligent mind and independent spirit are pitted against the sinking feeling you get when you can't button your jeans, or you can button them but you can't continue to breathe at the same time. Your intelligent mind and independent spirit aren't exactly winning. Sometimes they hold their own, and sometimes they whimper and cave in completely. Jane thinks you should spend more time having your hair done and less time thinking about whether or not having to sleep on steel rods might affect your brain.

Anything over ten and you are almost surely the sort of woman who will arrive at a party with a paper bag over your head if you got caught in a sudden shower on your way there and your make-up has been ruined. If you get on the bus and then discover that you've got a run in your stocking, you get off the bus and go back home. You never leave the house without putting on your face, doing your hair, and changing your outfit two or three times. You may even sleep in your make-up. On the other hand, you probably don't sleep. You probably lie awake all night, wondering if your hair's turning grey or if oranges make you fat. You're going to hate forty. And if you're already forty and you think you hate it, just imagine what sixty-five's going to be like.

3.

The Lifetime Diet: How, Why, and Whither

Sugar and Spice and Everything Nice

Men are taught early in life to obsess about women's bodies. Ooh, ahh, look at those tits. As a direct result of this, women are also taught early in life to obsess about women's bodies, especially their own.

They are taught, as well (as we have already seen in Chapter Two), that there are certain rules of dress, conduct and presentation that apply to them that do not apply to boys.

Boys, for example, are given lorries and guns and space stations to play with; girls are given Sindy dolls (Have you ever taken a really good, clinical look at the body of a Sindy doll? Why do *you* think she looks like that?) and toy lipsticks.

Boys aspire to role models as varied as James Dean, Neil Armstrong, Superman, Winston Churchill, Meatloaf, Indiana Jones, Salvador Dali, Elvis Presley, Albert Einstein, Samuel Beckett, Jesse James and Mahatma Gandhi; girls are given the likes of Cher, Samantha Fox, Kylie Minogue and the woman in the chocolate flake commercial.

Girls are taught through advertisements, television, films, music, and daily life just what being a girl is all about (looking good and being sexy) — and just what the criteria of feminine beauty are (and that, no matter what the changing requirements of fashion may be, fat is never one of them). A female human may start out as an ordinary person, but the moment she is given her first My Own Little Beauty Shop for Christmas, or picks up that women's magazine in the dentist's waiting room and learns the Ten Commandments of Good Grooming, she begins to change. The moment she realizes that people seeing a woman pass by never say, 'Wow, you wouldn't believe how intelligent she is!', or 'You won't believe how tireless her efforts are on behalf of the whales,' or, 'That girl's got the soul of a saint,' she starts getting fussy about the blue of her shirt matching the blue of her socks. The moment she understands that what people do say when they see a woman pass by is, 'Oh dear, chubby wubby,' or 'Thighs like tree trunks,' or 'Wow, will you look at *that*?!', she stops eating breakfast. By the time she has absorbed the fact that the only people who are always reassuring her that beauty is only skin deep are either stunningly beautiful themselves or the mothers of unattractive daughters, she is not just a plain, ordinary old person anymore, but a fully fledged, feminine girl. 'Wow,' she thinks, kneeling on the sink and twisting her body into an unnatural position so she can check for nostril hairs, 'and I used to worry about the plight of the panda! 'Right,' she says, taking on board the information that Cher works fifteen hours a day to achieve that body, and that nobody thinks that's silly, 'forget relativistic quantum field theory, what I want to know is how to have thinner thighs.'

The Lifetime Diet

There are millions of otherwise normal, intelligent, relatively sane women in this world who went on their first diet around the time that they started acquiring secondary sex characteristics, and who have never looked back. For from the moment they bit into their first slice of crispbread and taped that first picture of a lithesome young beauty in a bathing suit to their bedroom mirror, from the moment they first turned to their best friend and said, 'Actually, I really like cottage cheese, don't you?', their lives have been focused on one thing and one thing only. Others might worry about the destruction of Amazonia or the demise of the finback whale, but not they. They worry about being fat. Others might from time to time give a thought to abandoned cats and dogs or the problems of the elderly in a society that is obsessed with youth, but not they. They worry about being fat. Others might lose sleep thinking about the Greenhouse Effect and the state of the North Sea, but not they. They're scared out of their minds that they're going to gain weight.

And so begins the Lifetime Diet. A lifetime of being on a diet, blowing your diet, thinking about going on a diet, thinking about not going on a diet, feeling guilty that you're not on a diet, feeling guilty that you are on a diet but that you ate that chocolate cake anyway, being abnormally cheered up by little things like the sight of Cher eating a container of ice cream in *The Witches of Eastwick*. A lifetime of exercising, thinking about exercising, feeling guilty that you're not exercising, and threatening to exercise. There are few women in our society who have never bought a diet book, a calorie counter, an exercise book, a set of bathroom scales, or a dress in a size too small for encouragement. Few who have never finished a hearty meal and then turned to their best friend or the love of their life and wailed, 'Oh, why did you let me eat that?' Fewer still who have never stood in front of the mirror with a look of devastation on their imperfect faces, thinking: fat. Thinking: very fat. Thinking: hopelessly fat. Thinking: maybe I should kill myself. Thinking: I'll just finish the raspberry trifle and then, first thing tomorrow, I'm going on a diet.

Men may believe that they are women's favourite topic of conversation, but men have been wrong about more than one thing over the centuries. We women have more important things to talk about than men. Our hips. Our thighs. Our bums. What the best time of the day to weigh yourself is. Whether it's better to eat one substantial meal in the middle of the day, several tiny meals throughout the day, or nothing at all. Whether peanut sauce should be made illegal or not. 'Yes,' we say, 'David's got this really sexy smile, but did you know that brewer's yeast can help you lose weight?' 'Oh, yes, Ian's a really nice bloke, but did I tell you I'm going to swim to work instead of using the bus? It's meant to do wonders for your upper arms.' We are devastated if anyone suggests that there is more of us to love today than there was yesterday. 'It's water,' we scream. 'It's this dress.' 'All I said was that you'd put on a little weight,' says the unfortunate bearer of these bad tidings. 'You look good.' We throw the nearest object at his or her head. 'You always want to get at me, don't you?' we wail. 'You can never say anything nice.'

Let's face it. If your average woman knew as much about sexual politics as she does about the number of calories in a slice of cheesecake, this society would be a matriarchy.

What Is Real and What Is Not

'Don't you think you're getting a little carried away as usual, Serena?' asks Jane. 'You're making people who have no more than a healthy and understandable concern about their bodies sound like freaks.'

Maybe Jane's right. Maybe I am getting carried away. After all, in every other respect lifetime dieters are perfectly normal, wonderful people. They are doctors and dentists, sales assistants and business executives, famous hostesses and models, physicists and journalists, secretaries and nurses, carpenters and musicians, mothers and barristers. You could pass them on the street, or sit next to them in a restaurant, or even live with them for a long time without thinking there was anything strange going on. They don't look peculiar. They don't seem to be weird. Their lips don't move when they read and they don't carry bags of light bulbs around with them. 'Oh,' you say to yourself, 'there goes a normal, ordinary person.'

'And anyway,' says Jane, 'I think most people would have to agree that a fat person is not a pretty sight.'

That, of course, is a matter of opinion. But it is also, of course, irrelevant here. For we are not talking about fat people: we are talking about lifetime dieters.

There's a difference?

Of course there's a difference.

Fat people are fat. Some are fat because of traitorous glands or unreliable metabolic rates, in which case a diet is as useful to them as a skipping rope to a natterjack toad. Some of them are fat because they eat a lot and they enjoy eating it. They don't dither back and forth between the vegetable samosas and the lamb tikka, they have both, you only live once. They don't say, 'Oh, no thank you, I prefer my apple crumble plain', they say, 'Cream *and* ice cream, ta, very much. Oh, maybe just a bit more.' You never see them leaving half a meal untouched. Fat people may be periodically goaded and shamed onto diets by caring family and friends, but they usually don't like the experience all that much and aren't all that interested in making it their vocation.

Lifetime dieters, on the other hand, are not fat. In between Geena Davis and Marlon Brando are a multitude of body shapes and sizes, none neither more nor less intrinsically attractive than the next, and it is in that 'inbetween' that most lifetime dieters are to be found. Some could be called pudgy, and some could be called plump, but few of them would actually have trouble sharing a table for two with herself.

In fact, if someone were to point out a lifetime dieter to you and to ask you to consider her eating habits, you would probably say, 'Oh, well, I guess they're pretty ordinary. You know, normal.' You might imagine her sitting down to a bowl of cereal and a slice of toast in the morning, just like anybody else. You might picture her taking a break from work at eleven for a packet of crisps or a coffee and a doughnut, just like anybody else. You would probably guess that at lunch time she has a sandwich and a piece of fruit, or maybe something grilled with a salad and a freshly baked roll, as almost anyone might do. You think she eats supper. You assume that if you went to see a film with this person the two of you would share a box of popcorn. You think that, like the chap in the song, the lifetime dieter eats when she's hungry and drinks when she's dry.

But she doesn't. She has all sorts of taboos, habits and endearing little fetishes. She never eats the olive in her martini. She never eats the cherry on the ice cream sundae. She eats the topping from the pizza but not the crust. She stands in front of the fridge and eats half a cake and the remains of the tuna casserole, but she finds it hard to sit down to a big meal.

She often doesn't like to be seen eating at all. One day you go to lunch with her and she can barely get through the mixed salad without dressing. 'Oh,' she sighs, smiling a little smugly at your clean plate, 'I am *so* full.' And yet the next night the two of you go to a film and the one time you manage to get your hand into the popcorn box she practically bites off your fingers. 'I don't know what's wrong with me tonight,' she says, 'I just can't stop eating.' And before she does eat anything, the lifetime dieter almost always says, 'I shouldn't eat this.' After she eats something, she almost always says, 'I shouldn't have eaten that.' If you say, 'You look wonderful!', she'll say, 'I'm fat.' If you say, 'But you're not fat,' she'll say, 'Humpf.' If you say, 'So what if you're a little bit chunky?' she'll smash the remote control over your head and then lock herself in the bedroom for the next fourteen hours. If you say, 'Oh come on, that's not a very big piece of pie,' she'll say, 'That slice of pie has exactly 568 calories, and that's assuming they haven't brushed the crust with butter.' You look down at the offending slice of pie, afraid to ask if that includes the raisins or not. If you say, 'Um, Jane, I was just sort of casually wondering, what happened to that family-size bag of crisps that was in the cupboard?', she'll burst into tears.

If I Only Have One Life to Live, Let Me Live It on a Diet

Some people are obsessed with sex. Some people are obsessed with power. Some people are obsessed with money. Thousands of people are obsessed with Elvis Presley. Norman Mailer is obsessed with Marilyn Monroe. But the compulsive dieter is obsessed with food. Food and her thighs. She thinks about them all the time. To her a diet is not what, when or how much you eat, it is a way of life. Like Zen.

'Like Zen?' you ask.

Well, something like Zen. Unlike Zen, it doesn't lead to inner peace and tranquility. But like Zen it does inform every aspect of a person's being.

A recent poll of a random group of fifteen intelligent, attractive, mature and independent women with good jobs, okay senses of humour and strong senses of self, revealed that these fifteen women had been on a diet for a cumulative total of 333 years and 4 months. This is an average of 22.22 years each. Roughly. None of these women are dead yet, and none of them look as though they're about to throw away their mirrors, their scales, their tape measures, their Jane Fonda Workout tape, or their calorie counters. Or their guilt.

'22.22 years of cottage cheese and lettuce?' you ask.

'22.22 years of pineapple? Doesn't it make you turn yellow or something?'

'22.22 years of boiled chicken and all the bean sprouts you can eat?'

Well, no, of course not. When I say that going on a diet is not a temporary regimen but a way of life, I don't mean that you actually exist on 1,000 calories a day for the next thirty years. What I mean is that you think about being on a diet for the next thirty years. You question every mouthful of pasta. You can't bite into a piece of German Chocolate Cake without weeping. You jog the fourteen miles home from your cousin Mary's wedding — where the champagne has flowed like water and the buffet would have perked up Henry the Eighth — and then you stay up all night checking in the mirror to see if your bum is growing. You drive everybody who knows you crazy because you will never eat a whole anything. You take the filling out of the bread. You eat the bolognese but leave the spaghetti. You scrape the cheese and spinach filling out of sixteen little raviolis and mumble something about being allergic to wheat. The biscuit tin is filled with halves of biscuits. Little bits are hacked off the baguette, but no slices. In any bag of crisps, you will only eat the broken ones. People hate to invite you to dinner because they never know whether or not you're on a diet this week, and, if you are, which one. Is this the one where you can eat all the calories you want as long as they're in an avocado? Or is this the one where you can eat all he calories you want as long as you don't eat one gram of fat? Or is this the one where all you can eat is spinach and three ounces of peaches? You can never just sit down and eat. 'I'll pay for this later,' you say. 'How many calories do you think there is in Peking Duck if I don't use the pancake?' you want to know. You're convinced that you once stuck to the celery and water diet for two solid weeks and gained five pounds. The first thing you notice about anyone is whether or not they're likely to pass the pinch-an-inch test.

What you eat, how much you eat, and what effect it has on your hips is the dominant force in your life. You may be thin, you may be the perfect weight for your height and frame, you may be pleasantly plump or a little chunky or well-endowed, it doesn't matter. You always feel fat. You may hate to admit it, but you think Nancy Reagan had a point. You will never be happy with your bum. Or your breasts. Or your chubby little arms. It takes one person, a perfect stranger even, smiling at you evenly and saying, 'Putting on a little weight, aren't we, Pandora?', to send you under your duvet in sobs. Gaining weight makes you suicidal. 'I don't understand it,' you wail, 'I didn't eat a thing all day!' Maintaining your weight makes you unhappy. 'No matter what I do,' you moan, 'I stay the same.' Losing weight makes you even more unhappy. 'Oh my God,' you moan, chaining yourself to the bedpost, 'now I have to worry about putting it all back on.'

I can hear the non-lifetime dieters shuffling in amazement. 'You're kidding, right?' they ask. '*Thin* people, too?'

Take Jane for a for-instance. To look at Jane, you would think she was just your ordinary, run-of-the-mill, attractive, thirtysomething woman. Yes, you might look at her and think, I bet it takes her forty-five minutes to leave the house, even if she's just going around the corner for a paper, because it must take her that long just to get her eyelashes on. You might think, I'll wager you anything she can't talk to her mother on the telephone unless she's just put on clean underwear. You might nod your head wisely and say, if she doesn't own fifty-eight pairs of shoes I'm Daryl Hannah. But you would never think fat. You would never think, there is a woman who doesn't need a couch to sit on. You would never think, there is a woman who is losing the battle of the bulge. Cute, you'd think. Nice shape. I'll bet she looks great in satin slips, you'd speculate.

My friend Jane has been on a diet since she was eight years old. At her eighth birthday party her Uncle Walter, seeing her tucking into her third slice of cake, avec ice cream, said, 'Hey, Jane, if you don't watch out you're going to look just like Aunt Sheena.' Uncle Walter laughed. Aunt Sheena had a build that would have found favour with Reubens. No one in the family, except Uncle Walter, ever said the name Sheena without adding 'of the jungle'. Jane, like everyone else, loved Aunt Sheena. Aunt Sheena was a kind, generous and warm-hearted person. You hear a variety of opinions about Jerry Hall, but about Aunt Sheena the world was unanimous. A gem. One in a million. The sort of human being who gives the species a good name. But though thousands of women would give their eye teeth, their birthrights, and the chance of a date with Mel Gibson to look like Jerry Hall, no woman in the history of Western civilization ever wanted to look like Aunt Sheena. Right then and there, Jane put down her spoon, shoved her plate into the middle of the table, and went into the bathroom and thew up.

'You see,' says Jane, 'even at that tender age I knew that Aunt Sheena was a failure as a woman. Men never looked at her. Kids made fun of her. She was always identified by the word "fat". My mother would say, "That's my sister, over there," and the person she was speaking to would never say, "You mean the one in the red dress"' or "You mean the one carrying the boa constrictor?" The person she was speaking to would say, "You mean the fat lady?"'

But, Jane, wasn't your Aunt Sheena a brilliant mathematician?

'A genius.'

And didn't she single-handedly raise money to bring solar energy and a new prosperity to a poor Nepalese village teetering on the brink of destruction?

'That's right, that's the same Aunt Sheena.'

And didn't your Uncle Walter love her?

'Yes, that's true. But they'd been married for centuries, and they had all these children and this notorious sex life, you'd expect him to love her.'

Didn't Mother Teresa call your Aunt Sheena a saint?

'Yes, I do think she said something like that.'

But if all those things are true, how can you say that Aunt Sheena was a failure?

'Construction workers never whistled at her.'

You say, 'Wow.' You say, 'I don't believe it.' You say, 'I've never heard of anything so crazy. What's wrong with her?'

'Be careful how you go here, Serena,' says Jane. 'Let's not forget that you've been on your diet since you were eleven-and-a-half.'

I won't forget. How could I?

'Wait a minute! Wait a minute!' say you. 'Serena, *you've* been on a diet since you were eleven-and-a-half?'

Of course I have. How else do you think I know so much about it?

4.

Food and You: The First Quiz

And what about you?

What sort of relationship do you have with food? Do you like food and does it like you? Can you take it or leave it? Do you eat because food consumption is a good idea if a person wants to stay alive; or do you eat, when you eat, because you just lost a big account or there's nothing good on television? Do you think of food as nutrition, or do you think of it as the enemy within?

What sort of relationship do you have with your body? Do you like your body? Does your body feel pretty kindly towards you? Or is your body treacherous and unreliable? Does your body punish you every time you eat a slice of chocolate gateau? Do you punish it every time you eat a slice of chocolate gateau? Do you wish your body belonged to someone else — someone whom you don't like?

Here's a quiz that will help you assess your attitude to both food and your flesh, and at the same time allow you to discover what your DQ (Diet Quotient) really is. Just in case you don't already know or have been kidding yourself along.

What follows are some typical situations that can — and do — happen to anyone. All you have to do is select the answer that best describes how you would react were it to happen to you. Keep in mind that the continued progress and prosperity of mankind is best served by total honesty.

1. You are a dedicated dieter. The first thing you do every morning when you get up is weigh yourself. Then you weigh yourself again. After that you kick the scales across the bathroom and put your dressing gown back on and the clip back in your hair. You know the caloric value of every edible substance from tree bark to Zeitgeist Soup. You are an expert on hidden calories; you never even accidentally swallow toothpaste. And then what happens? Christmas happens. Christmas, as all serious dieters know, is the Holiday of Hell. You've got to do something about that damn egg at Easter, and Valentine's Day is a little problematical (unless your eyes are too close together or you haven't worn a size ten since you were thirteen, in which case you probably don't have a boyfriend and so are in no danger of receiving a heart-shaped box of calories). But it is Christmas that tests the mettle of the perpetual slimmer like no other time. Mince pies, Christmas pud, alcohol, brandy sauce, that endless round of parties with deep-fried mushrooms and mayonnaise-based dips. You'd think Christmas had been especially created to triple the profits of Weight Watchers in the new year. Is it any wonder that the Christmas season is known for its high suicide rate? It's all those poor people who have come through the entire autumn on a couple of bunches of carrots and a case of crispbread and then find themselves standing in the supermarket, right in the spot where the sugar substitutes usually live, staring at an entire aisle of fruit cakes, candies, and holiday treats. How can they not

snap? But you don't snap. You're a pro when it comes to avoiding the temptations of the too-much flesh. You only drink water at parties. You only eat nuts with shells since there's so much time and work involved in getting just one. You dig your nails into your palms whenever someone comes near you with a bowl of crisps or anything small in pastry. You eat three bunches of celery before you go anywhere so that even the salmon mousse looks unappealing. It's Christmas Eve and so far your only indulgence has been one mince pie from which you first wiped the sugar and half of which you stuck into the soil of the plant you were sitting beside. Forty-five calories, not too bad. And then the doorbell rings and you answer it and there is a delivery person with a five-pound box of hand-dipped Belgian chocolates, made with real cream and fruit. It is from someone who loves you very much, but who has been out of the country for a while, and who still thinks of you as the same person you were the last time he saw you, when you were three pounds overweight, became headachey and tetchy if you missed a meal, and loved hand-dipped Belgian chocolates made with real cream and fruit. You smile at the delivery person as though you are happy to see him. 'Oh, thank you,' you say. 'Have a Merry Christmas!' And then you:

a. carry the box back into the house and put it in the fridge. This isn't so bad, you tell yourself. It means you don't have to actually go out and *buy* anything to have in the house in case friends drop by. In fact, you figure you can probably get rid of half the box on your brother alone. There is a slight danger in this, of course, because you may relent and eat one or two yourself, especially towards the end when the box has been opened and you're anxious to get it emptied. But it is a nice present, even if you'd have preferred an exercise bike. And it probably cost nearly as much as an exercise bike. So what else can you do? And anyway, if you can't have a chocolate now and then, what's the point of living in the Western world? You might as well be living in a cave in the Himalayas.

b. put on your coat, your mittens and your woolly hat, tuck the chocolates under your arm, and march down the street to your friend Emma, who has four children, all under twelve. You give her the chocolates, even though you know that the children won't eat them (they're too good) and she will probably give them to someone else because she's been on a diet since 1973.

c. march smartly into the kitchen and throw the box into the rubbish without a second's hesitation. About two hours later, hearing the siren call of the coffee creams whispering your name, you goose-step over to the rubbish, open the box of chocolates, and drop them, en masse, into the bin. Approximately forty-five minutes later, while making yourself a cup of black tea, you hear the truffles saying, quite distinctly for truffles, 'We're not really dirty, we landed on top of the bag the celery came in.' You grit your teeth. And then you yank the plastic bag from the bin and race out to the dustbins with it. You stuff it in and slam the lid down. You hurry back into the house and lock yourself in.

d. fill the sink with hot water and drop the chocolates into it. From experience you know that half an hour in a tub of hot water is sufficient to make even the most irresistible box of candy in the world about as appetizing as a tin of slugs. You go into the bathroom and start scrubbing the tiles with a toothbrush to give you something to do until the half-hour is up.

e. put the box on the kitchen table and go back to what you were doing. For about three minutes. Then a flat little voice in your head says, 'Oh, come on, what's the harm in just *looking* at them?' So you open the box. You look at them. They look lovely. That same piggy little voice says, 'One. What's the fuss about eating one?' So you eat one. When you come to, about twenty minutes later, the only thing left in the box are those little paper cups and you're unbuttoning your skirt. You console yourself with the fact that you hated every crumb and that you feel so ill it's unlikely you'll be able to eat again for at least three days. You're certainly safe from the Christmas pudding. You wonder if moving to the Himalayas might not be a viable idea.

2. Your best friend invites you over to dinner. It's not going to be a big do, she tells you, just a few really close friends. She thought she'd have it on Friday night, at her country cottage, though she has to warn you that the weatherman is predicting heavy snow so it may be necessary to stay the entire weekend. And, oh, yes, she really really hopes you can come, because Bono will be there and she knows how fond you are of him and how much you've always wanted to meet him. The first question you ask is:

   a. 'What time?' The second is: 'Is he bringing his wife?'

   b. 'You'll be serving the meal by candlelight, won't you?'

   c. 'Oh my God, what am I going to wear?'

   d. 'What are you making?' 'Pardon me?' says your best friend. 'Did you ask me what I'm *making*? To eat?' 'That's right,' you say. 'I'm not coming if you're making that lethal fettuccine alfredo with all the butter and the cream and the pound of parmesan.' 'Er, Jane,' says your best friend. 'You did hear me, didn't you? I said Bono is going to be there. I was going to make sure that he sat next to you.' 'I'm not sitting next to anybody,' you say rather waspishly. 'Not unless you swear on Audrey Eyton's life that you're not serving anything with cheese or cream sauce.'

   e. 'Why couldn't you have told me sooner? That only gives me six days to get ready!'

3. You are standing in the chemist's, when you overhear the female assistant say to the woman in front of you, 'This Royal Jelly is really expensive, isn't it?' 'It's not the cost that bothers me,' says the woman. 'What worries me is that I think it's fattening.' The assistant and you both look at the woman. 'Fattening?' repeats the assistant 'Royal Jelly? But it comes from bees.' 'So does honey,' says the woman. She shakes her head with some conviction. 'Last time I used it I just know I put on weight.' 'You did?' you say. 'You put on weight?' echoes the assistant. 'That's right,' says the woman. And now I'm on this diet and I want to lose at least three stone....' You look at the woman. The assistant looks at the woman. You and the assistant look at each other. This woman can't weigh much more than nine stone. Nor is she a midget. 'What you do,' says the assistant knowingly, 'is weigh yourself before you start the course, and then if you've gained weight at the end you know it's the jelly.' 'Um,' says the woman, that same look coming into her eyes that Indiana Jones gets when someone says, 'Just pick up the snake, Indy.' 'That's the way to do it,' you agree, though you yourself, do not, in fact, own a set of scales as a matter of principle. 'But I'm on a diet,' says the woman. The assistant looks at you as if to say, 'So who isn't?' 'Well there you go,' says the assistant, 'as long as you don't binge or anything....' There is a sharp intake of breath and three wry smiles at the mention of binge. 'Oh, no,' says the woman quickly, 'of course I wouldn't binge.' 'Of course not,' say

you. 'Of course not,' says the assistant. And then the assistant says once more, 'Just weigh yourself before you start the Royal Jelly.' 'Er,' says the woman, 'weigh myself.' The assistant looks at the till. You look at the reduced cosmetics. 'Weigh myself,' the woman mumbles as she wanders towards the door. 'Weigh myself.' As soon as the door shuts behind the woman your eyes meet the eyes of the assistant and:

a. even you, a woman who has been been heard to remark that she thinks Tom Cruise is a little on the chubby size, has to laugh. 'You think she really wants to lose three stone?' you ask. The assistant shrugs her bony little shoulders. 'Doesn't everybody?' she inquires politely. 'Well,' you say, 'I've heard of people being terrified of a double fudge brownie but I've never heard of anyone who was frightened of being weighed.' 'You haven't?' says the assistant. You put your basket, containing three moisturizers, a skin toner and a hair lightener, on the counter. 'No.' 'You didn't hear about that woman in Birmingham who was arrested for throwing her scales into the canal?' 'They arrested her for drowning her scales?' 'They thought it was a body. They'd been watching her for months. Since she buried her last set of scales in the garden.' You fiddle with a tube of foot lotion by the till. 'No, I didn't hear about that.' 'You didn't hear about the woman who divorced her husband because he got drunk at a party and made her weigh herself in front of everyone?' You're kidding,' you say. 'She *divorced* him?' 'That was after she tried to kill him with the stereo,' says the assistant. 'Wow,' you sigh. 'I didn't hear about that either.' 'Where do you live?' asks the assistant. You shrug. 'Around the corner.'

b. you say, 'I don't think Royal Jelly can possibly be fattening, do you?' The assistant shakes her head. 'It does seem unlikely,' she agrees. 'On the other hand,' you say, looking down at the tube in your basket, 'it is pretty expensive, isn't it?' 'Well, I didn't like to say anything,' says the assistant, 'but did you know that according to *Cosmopolitan* there are times when water can be fattening?'

c. she shakes her head. 'What a world,' she says. 'I tell you, you meet all kinds, working with the public. And I thought the woman who came in to complain that her iron tablets were making her retain water was something. But Royal Jelly being fattening!' You slide your basket onto the counter a little stiffly. You purse your lips. 'Excuse me,' you say, 'but it just so happens that *I* was the woman who complained that the iron tablets were making me retain water, and it happened to be true.' 'Oh,' says the assistant. 'I mean, I know. I wasn't talking about you. I was talking about someone else whose iron tablets weren't making her retain water.'

d. she says, 'Now I've heard everything! Royal Jelly fattening! Next thing you know they'll be saying that lettuce and cottage cheese make you put on weight.' 'Don't laugh,' you say. 'I was on this diet once where all you could eat was raw vegetables and eight ounces of low-fat cottage cheese a day, and I gained a stone and a half.' 'A stone and a half?' repeats the assistant. 'On raw vegetables and low-fat cottage cheese?' 'Absolutely true,' you say, and slip the Royal Jelly back on the shelf.

e. you laugh, but it is a slightly high-pitched, nervous laugh. 'Do you weigh yourself very often?' you ask the assistant.

4. You have had a bad day. If there was anything that could have gone wrong that didn't go wrong, then you can be sure that it didn't go wrong because it's biding its time so that when it does go wrong the effect will not only be ten times worse, it'll catch you completely by surprise as well. From the moment you boarded the bus this morning, someone has been yelling at you about something. The bus driver wouldn't give you change. The woman next to you claimed you were taking up more than your share of the seat. When you arrived at work, your boss was screaming about some little mistake that anyone could have made and Annabel Jackfrost wouldn't speak to you because she heard what you said about her hair (which is unfair, because everyone agrees that it looks like a cheap wig). Your boyfriend called to tell you that he's fallen in love with someone a lot thinner and prettier than you, and your mother rang to find out if you

wanted her to give you a weekend at a health clinic (which your mother, old-fashioned as she is, still insists on calling a fat farm) for your birthday. You broke two finger nails and your left eyelash came off in your morning tea. You met that cute bloke from Accounts, the one who is always asking you out (but you have never gone, because of your boyfriend), in the sandwich bar and he invited you to his wedding to Michelle Pfeiffer's sister (who looks a lot like Michelle but who, everyone says, inherited the real looks in the family). By the time the big hand is on the six and the little hand is on the five, you want nothing more than to get inside your flat, bolt the door behind you, and crawl under the duvet. But before you slink into the relative safety of your own home you have to stop at the super-market and buy a tin of food for the cat. You:

a. buy a tin of food for the cat. Because you've had such a bad day, you buy yourself half a bottle of wine and a bumper pack of spicy cheese puffs as a special treat. When you get home, you feed the cat, drag the duvet into the living room so you can lie on the couch and watch a Marx Brothers video while you're recuperating, and dive under, cheesie puffs crunching.

b. buy the cat her favourite gourmet seafood platter and then, tempted by the bakery section, you decide to pop into the gym for a workout on the weights to get rid of your feelings of aggression, hostility and cata-clysmic depression. Tonight, as luck would have it, the gym is filled with women who don't know what the words 'big bum' or 'endomorph' mean. They ride their bikes and row their boats and climb their invisible mountains not, you can tell, to tone up lazy muscles and tone down exuberant hips, but to show off their leotards, lycra leggings and ribs. By the time you start back towards home the depression you were experiencing earlier is but a slingshot compared to a neutron bomb. So, even though you know you shouldn't, because of the Amazon rain-forest, you stop at McDonald's and have a diet coke, a burger, two large fries and an apple pie. You feel better almost immediately. Though not for long.

c. buy the cat six tins of the most expensive brand (even though you know she has a personal policy of only eating half a tin of anything that costs as much as the equivalent human food), and buy a few things you need for the house as well. What should have cost forty-nine pence comes to a grand total of twenty quid. You lumber home with your shopping, put it away, feed the cat (who takes two mouthfuls before she goes back to sleep), and then tuck yourself up under the duvet with a good book and a packet of rice cakes, a wedge of cheese, a bowl of fruit and a box of bourbon creams. By the time the heroine is discovering just what a jerk the hero is, you are on your third pear, feeling more depressed than ever, and wondering if you should flush the cookies down the toilet while you still can.

d. tear through the supermarket like the Nazi war machine zipping through Poland, flinging into your cart everything that is edible and doesn't need more than four minutes of preparation, decimating entire shelves and terrorizing more sedate shoppers who believe that one container of ice cream at a time is more than enough for anybody as you hurl yourself into the desserts freezer with a strangled cry. You spend twenty-five pounds and ninety-five pence (which includes the salmon-flavoured cereal-and-horse-ears for the cat and two rolls of toilet paper, a grand total of one pound and one penny). By the time the credits are coming up on the video you rented so you'd have something to do while you were eating, you have consumed twenty-four pounds and twenty pence worth of groceries (to do credit to your mother, who raised you with a basic sense of nutrition, not all of this was snack food: there were several tuna sandwiches, a tub of herb and garlic cheese and a tin of baked beans among the crisps, pretzels, cheese whirly-gigs, potato munchies and chocolate chocolate chip cookies). You fall asleep with a box of miniature treacle tarts still clutched in your hand. You dream that you are Dorothy in the Wizard of Oz. But instead of fleeing home because everybody's being mean to you, you are fleeing because you cleaned out the local grocery store and are searching for a place to shop where no one knows you or the terrible truth about you (that you have been breaking your diet for the last fifteen years). And instead of landing among the jolly Munchkins you land among the neurotic Thinkins. You kill the bad witch by falling on her, just like in the movie, except that you didn't need a house. The Thinkins all run away from you because they're afraid you're going to eat them. You might very well eat them (there seems to be an appalling lack of chocolate bars in Oz) but you can't move fast enough to catch them because of your vast size. You get really hungry, following that bloody yellow brick road. Every once in a while, the head of the Wicked Witch of the West hovers above you, cackling, 'We'll see who's going on a diet, Dorothy, heh-heh-heh-heh-heh.' At last you see what looks like a supermarket. 'Whoopee!' you cry. 'I'm saved.' But when you get inside you are confronted by aisle after aisle of crispbreads and bunches of watercress. You look at Toto. Toto, who'd been hoping for a little mincemeat himself, looks at you. 'Toto,' you say, 'this isn't Safeway.' When you wake up you discover that you've eaten the treacle tarts in your sleep. You start wondering if there is some crime you could commit that would put you inside for a year or two, no visitors or gifts of food allowed.

e. decide not to risk going into a store that sells food in the mood you're in. 'The cat can eat a tin of tuna,' you tell yourself. But while looking for the tin of tuna you discover that your larder is not as empty as you'd thought. There's that bag of sultanas you bought the year you were thinking of making a fruit cake for Christmas, just to prove to yourself and your mother that you could do it without eating all the glacé cherries before you got them into the batter. There's a bag of walnuts you bought when you were going to treat yourself to that special pasta once you'd lost two stone. There's the muesli you bought when you were on the F-Plan diet. There's six tins of pineapple you bought when you were on the pineapple diet. There's the jar of peanut butter and box of chocolate covered chestnuts you bought because someone told you that just as a person cannot be considered a non-smoker until she can carry a pack of cigarettes around without lighting up, a person cannot be considered a non-potential-fat person if she can't keep her favourite fattening things in the cupboard without eating them. You decide to spend the night in the bus station, where how much you eat is at least controlled by the amount of change you have on you. You make sure that you don't have more than twelve thousand calories on you.

5. Your best friend has been very ill with the flu. Two weeks of fever, headache, chills, throbbing limbs, nausea and exhaustion. You have, of course, phoned her every day to make sure she hasn't died, but she's been in no shape for a long conversation. You've stopped by to see if she needed anything a couple of

times, but she's been too weak to do more than lift her head an inch or two off the pillow and whisper, 'Ahhh.' At last she recovers. She phones you up to tell you the good news. The first thing you say is:

a. 'Serena, I'm so glad you're feeling better.'

b. 'You know, Serena, it might be a good idea to go swimming or something once you feel up to it. All that bed rest is bad for your muscle tone.'

c. 'Is your skin still that funny colour?'

d. 'How much weight did you lose, you bitch?'

e. 'It usually takes a few days before you start looking human again.'

6. You've been on this diet for six highly successful weeks. 1,500 calories a day, with a glass of white wine and one plain digestive biscuit allowed on Sundays as a reward. You can get on the scales in the morning without keeping one foot on the floor. You can't yet button that slinky green dress, but you can get it over your hips. And then the worst thing that could possibly happen — short of the people in the flat below yours turning their home into an Italian restaurant and letting you eat there for free whenever you want — happens. You are invited to dinner by a woman who thinks that she hasn't made enough food unless the entire British Army could drop by unexpectedly and not one man would have to go away hungry. You:

a. gracefully accept the invitation without making one emotional comment about your diet or your hips. It is only one meal, after all. And the mere fact that your friend thinks a serving is something that looms seven inches above the surface of your plate and comes close to falling off the edges doesn't mean that you have to eat it all. Does it?

b. gracefully decline the invitation, pleading a previous engagement. This isn't easy to do, because this woman is not only a generous but an excellent cook, but you feel it's the best way round the problem. Maybe in a year or two you'll be able to eat a real meal without worrying that you're immediately going to gain twelve pounds, but not yet.

c. say, 'Of course, Pandora, I'd love to come.' Two days later you call back and say, 'I'm sorry, but I've come down with this beastly cold. I don't think I'll be able to make it after all.' Pandora, says, 'Oh, Jane, I'm so sorry to hear that. If you do feel better by Friday, please come, won't you? I'm making that aubergine parmigiana you love so much. And that special garlic bread with the herbs and paprika?' All day Friday you play the 'Should I Go — Should I Not Go?' game. If you go you'll make a pig of yourself on garlic bread and fried aubergine and in forty-five minutes destroy six weeks' worth of willpower and starvation. If you don't go, you'll be so upset to have missed such a great dinner that you'll wind up eating a family pack of Mars bars and then spend the rest of the night on the rowing machine. You go, you eat, and the man you've been invited to this dinner for the sole purpose of meeting thinks you either don't speak English or have the IQ of a pencil because it never occurs to him that the reason you don't join in the conversation is because you're trying to keep a mental running total of your calorie intake.

d. decide on what you consider not merely a reasonable compromise but an idea that could revolutionize the entire concept of dieting as we know it. You permit yourself to eat only one third of your aubergine. One third you cut into neat little pieces and chew carefully and slowly, just as the books tell you, and the other two-thirds you slip into the napkin on your lap. You eat the crust from the garlic bread and unobtrusively put the lethal portion in the napkin too. Dessert — zabaglione — is a little trickier, but you feel reasonably secure by the time dessert arrives that there is a solid enough foundation on the napkin that the zabaglione won't soak right through to your pure silk dress. And you're right, it doesn't soak through. Unfortunately, the reason it doesn't soak through is that the aubergine, the tomato sauce and the excessively buttered garlic bread (trust Pandora, the cow) have already done that. Everybody thinks its pretty weird that you refuse to leave the table after the meal is over. Pandora thinks it's downright peculiar that

you sit there by yourself, smiling woodenly
while everyone else sits on the floor playing
Trivial Pursuit till three in the morning. By
the time you get home even your underwear
smells like pizza and you're so depressed
about the fool you made of yourself that
you eat all the cold aubergine you managed
to stuff into your handbag while Pandora
was showing the other guests out.

e. have a good long talk with yourself. 'Self,'
you say, 'you are an adult human, not a
warthog, not a Russian wolfhound, not a
boa constrictor. You can go to a dinner
party without over-indulging yourself. The
purpose of going on a diet was not so that
you could never eat in public again, but so
that you could. Tell Pandora you'd love to
go.' So you tell Pandora you'd love to go.
And you have a wonderful time. You talk
and laugh and make merry. You dump half a
cellar of salt over your aubergine so that it
is difficult even for you to eat more than a
few mouthfuls. 'My goodness, Jane,' says
Pandora while you are helping her clear the
table, 'you've got the appetite of a bird.'
You look at her closely to make sure she
isn't being facetious, but the word humming-
bird doesn't so much as hover on her lips.
'It's this fantastic diet I've been on,' you say.
'It's totally changed my relationship with
food.'

7. You are doing your weekly shopping. There
you go, up the fruit and veg aisle, and down
the pasta, grain and cereals, up the household

goods and down the pet foods. You select your items and toss them into your trolley with a practised air. Webb lettuce, not iceberg; Jaffa oranges, not Seville; environmentally friendly washing-up liquid, not that villianous kind. And then you come upon the aisle of the chewy cereal bars. You:

a. brake suddenly. Oh, I don't believe it, you say to yourself, apricot and chocolate chip, my favourite! You reach for a packet with a happy smile.

b. are just about to go for the apple and raisin when you notice that the trolley beside you is being driven by a rather chunky woman whose rather chunky husband is tossing chewy bars into their cart, as though confident that tomorrow will never come. Sitting in the cart, eating a packet of crisps, is a chunky child. You pull your hand back from the shelf as though you've been burnt, and turn back towards household goods.

c. reach for the apricot and chocolate bars, and immediately turn to the nutrition information notice to see how many calories they contain.

d. check the calories per bar of every variety from oat and straw to hazelnut and raisin. You select the one that has three fewer calories per bar than any of the others, even though you know they taste like something a horse might be fond of.

e. whizz right by. But by the time you reach the end of the aisle a little voice is saying,

'Chewy cereal bars are meant to be good for you.' 'They have honey in them,' you answer back. 'They're small,' says the voice, 'how much honey could there be?' 'I do like them,' you confess. 'Especially apricot and chocolate chip.' 'Go on,' the voice urges, 'treat yourself. You deserve something nice. All lettuce and cottage cheese makes Pandora a grumpy girl.' You start back. Halfway to the chewy bars shelf, you say out loud (and to the considerable surprise of several other shoppers), 'No, no, I really shouldn't. Honey *and* chocolate chips? What am I thinking of?' 'So don't get the ones with the chips,' says the voice. 'Get something else. For Pete's sake, they're barely the size of a pocket comb!' 'You're right,' you say. 'And I don't have to eat them all at once, do I?' 'Certainly not,' says the voice. You reach out and put the first packet of chewy bars that your hand touches into your trolley and move into the next aisle as quickly as you can.

8. You and Charlie are madly in love. You and Charlie are not only madly in love, but you have so much in common that it's hard to believe that you aren't the same person. You like Mozart, he likes Mozart. He likes windsurfing, you like windsurfing. He likes Jimmy Stewart, you like Jimmy Stewart. Since there's no point in wasting two apartments on you, you and Charlie get married. On your wedding night Charlie says in that dreamy, confident way that lovers often use to impart crucial

information, 'Darling, I certainly hope you're not going to turn to fat like your mother.' You blow into his ear and giggle. 'My mother's not fat,' you say. 'But she weighs more than eight stone,' says Charlie, the dreaminess beginning to vanish from his voice. You look over, curious. 'So?' Charlie looks surprised. 'Darling,' he says, 'we discussed this at some length the night we first made love. You know I don't think any woman should weigh more than eight stone.' He shudders. 'I find women with any extra fat on them physically repulsive.' 'My mother's not fat,' you say again. 'She has a rounded stomach,' says Charlie. 'I could never live with a woman with a rounded stomach.' Because you are looking at him so closely, you know he's not joking. You:

a. dump the champagne bucket over his head, get dressed, go home, and call your lawyer.

b. snuggle up against him. 'Don't worry, darling,' you coo, 'I'll never let myself go.'

c. excuse yourself for a minute, go into the bathroom and flush the wedding cake down the loo.

d. wait until Charlie has gone to sleep and then spend your wedding night alternately weighing yourself on the bathroom scales and looking through the Yellow Pages for a doctor who does tummy tucks.

e. think to yourself, what the hell? You were planning to spend the rest of your life on a diet anyway.

9. You are at a great party. The people are friendly, the music is good, and the wine doesn't taste like it was made in a chemical plant. You are standing in a corner of the room, having an absolutely fascinating conversation about portable telephones, when along comes the hostess with a tray of crackers topped with cream cheese and dead fish eggs. 'Thank you,' says the man with so many amusing stories about cordless phones, 'this looks delicious.' 'Oh, yummy,' says his wife. 'I just love party food. You don't have any of those little sausages, do you?' 'And how about you, Pandora?' says your charming hostess. 'I made them myself.' You:

a. take this opportunity to kill two birds with one stone and say, 'Actually, I was just on my way to the buffet table for another one of those amazing devilled eggs.' You turn to your companions. 'I'll be right back,' you lie.

b. 'Oh, um,' you mumble. Your hand hesitates, hovering in mid-air. Oh well, you think, they are small. How many calories can there be in six tiny fish eggs and a spoonful of cream cheese?

c. know without thinking that there are exactly 198 calories in six tiny fish eggs and a spoonful of cream cheese and one cracker. Unless, of course, it's low-fat cream cheese and low-cal caviar. Is it worth the risk? Just one? You shake your head. Oh, no,' you murmur, 'I really couldn't.' The hostess keeps smiling. She reminds you of your mother. You back into the man behind you. 'No, no,' you repeat, 'I'd better not.' Your hand still hovers. 'Well,' you say, looking over your shoulder to make sure no one's watching, 'maybe just half one.'

d. jump as though the hostess isn't waving a silver tray in your face but a loaded gun. 'Oh ugh ahh,' you stammer. 'No, really, they look lovely, I mean, they look really delicious, but I don't thi....' 'Oh come on,' grins your hostess, reminding you more and more of your mother, 'don't tell me you're on a diet again.' She laughs as though this is one of the funniest things she's heard in a long time. What you're not quite sure about is whether she thinks it's funny because you're so slender that the idea of you being on a diet is ludicrous, or if she thinks it's funny because you've been on a diet for so long and you've still got fat thighs.

e. take one, exclaiming over how delicious they look, but you only pretend to eat it.

10. You and one of your best friends decide to treat yourselves to dinner at your favourite restaurant. It's Monday, so you're on a diet. Your friend, one of the fifteen women ever born on the planet Earth whose only weight worry has been trying to put some on, is not on a diet. But you're not bothered. You have *The Restaurant Goer's Calorie Guide* in your pocket. You're foolproof. You have a wonderful dinner. Crisp, cold, fatless melon for starters. Charcoal-grilled sole for your main course. You decline the sautéed potatoes in

favour of boiled rice and a green salad, dressing on the side. You give your friend your roll. Your dieter's halo is blinding the waitress. You have a glass of white wine (the non-fattening kind). 'We should do this more often,' you say to your friend with a happy smile. 'Oh, yes,' she cries. 'We really should.' 'I'd forgotten how much I love this place,' you laugh. 'Me too,' agrees your friend. 'I don't understand why we haven't been here for so long,' you muse. 'Me neither,' says your friend. And then, just when you're feeling as good about your thighs as it is possible for you to feel this side of death, along comes the waitress with the dessert menu. Now you remember why you haven't been in this restaurant in so long. Its starters are mediocre. Its entrées are okay. Its desserts make strong men weep and women with a weakness for sweet things covered in chocolate pig out. Your friend, who if she felt about wine the way she feels about chocolate would be a member of Alcoholics Anonymous, orders the fudge brownie with chocolate ice cream and hot fudge sauce. (Your friend is not only overly fond of chocolate, she is also totally insensitive to the metabolic rates of others). You:

a. order the fruit salad.

b. moan and groan for approximately seven-and-a-half minutes. 'I shouldn't have anything,' you say. Your friend says nothing. The waitress looks at her nails. 'But the profiteroles here are world-famous, aren't they.' 'And with good reason,' says your friend. The waitress shifts her order pad to her other hand. 'Yes,' you sigh, 'but I really shouldn't. I mean, profiteroles with banana cream. My hips would never forgive me. I better not.' 'Okay,' says your friend. The waitress starts looking at your nails. 'On the other hand,' you say, suddenly noticing the triple-chocolate mousse, 'you only live once, right?' 'That's right,' says your friend. The waitress makes a noncommittal hum. A worrying thought occurs to you. 'Still,' you say, 'if I have only one life I don't want to live it looking like the Michelin Man.' Your friend laughs, as someone who lives in the desert will laugh when their pal who lives by the ocean worries about drowning. The waitress says, 'So, okay, ladies, what'll it be?' You order the fruit salad and a black coffee. 'I'll just have a tiny taste of yours when it comes,' you say to your friend.

c. order the profiteroles with banana cream. Then you change your mind. 'No, no,' you say to the waitress, 'not the profiteroles. Make it the chocolate cheesecake with raspberry sauce.' The waitress raises an eyebrow and scratches out profiteroles. She has written choc ches when you say, 'Oh, God, you're going to hate me, but could you change that to apple pie?' The waitress says, 'Sure, apple pie. With ice cream or cream?' 'Cream.' 'You're sure about that?' 'Yes, I'm sure,' 'Right,' says the waitress. 'That's one brownie and one apple pie with cream.' You say, 'Um.' The waitress and your friend both turn to you expectantly. 'Now what?' asks the waitress. 'Forget the cream,' you say. The waitress looks over at your friend. They exchange a glance. 'Apple pie, no cream,' says the waitress. She looks you straight in the eye. 'You're sure now, right?' 'Absolutely.' When your desserts come you decide just to eat the filling of your pie. You eat the filling. You immediately feel so fat that you eat the crust as well. Then you call the waitress back and order the profiteroles.

d.   order black coffee. 'You know me,' you say to your friend. 'I don't really have much of a sweet tooth.' The waitress brings your coffee and your friend's death by chocolate. Your friend looks up from manipulating a little bit of brownie, a little bit of ice cream and a lot of sauce on her spoon to find you gazing at her as Romeo once gazed at Juliet. 'You want a little taste?' she asks with a resigned sort of sigh. Your spoon is in your hand. 'You're sure you don't mind?' 'No,' says your friend, pushing her plate towards you. 'I don't mind.' As usually happens, you eat all of your friend's dessert. Which is her reason for not having come to this restaurant in so long. On the way home, you have a falling out because she refuses to see why she should be held responsible for you ingesting three million extra calories in one day.

e.   order the fruit salad and a black coffee. When you get home, still thinking of the profiteroles you would have ordered if you hadn't known you'd gain three pounds just smelling them, you eat a bag of sultanas.

11. You are on a diet. If you were living in, say, a cave in the Himalayas, by yourself, sticking to this diet would be as easy as inhaling a packet of custard creams when you're feeling depressed. Unfortunately, you are not tucked away in a Himalayan cave, far from super-stores and corner shops and bakeries. And you are not by yourself. You live with one man, two boys, a girl too young to yet realize that peanut butter and banana sandwiches threaten her life just as surely as CFCs, and a large dog. When these people and the four-legged waste disposal they call Rollo aren't packing it in like the famine starts tomorrow (never, of course putting on even a fraction of an ounce no matter how many helpings of lasagne or chocolate custard they shovel into their faces), you are actually quite fond of them.

But it is difficult to be fond of them when you're on a diet. Their constant presence in your home makes it hard to concentrate on the cottage cheese and celery sticks. In the morning you, an unfit and average-looking thirtysomething with the physique of a dumpling, sit at the table with the breakfast of a very fit, thin and beautiful twenty-year-old (one ounce of cereal, two ounces of juice, a cup of black coffee and a thin slice of toast, no butter, no jam, no honey) while your family devours soup bowls of cornflakes drowning in sugar and milk, stacks of buttered toast with jam dripping off the sides, and cups of tea so sweet the mugs are smiling. If you get through that without cracking you only need an ordinary amount of will power and divine help to get through the day, because unless it is a weekend you are usually alone with your apple and ounce of low-fat cheese at lunch time. (Although you have been known, in a pinch, to eat spaghetti or day-old cooked peas, you have never been tempted by Rollo's food.)

But just as Monday comes bouncing along directly after Sunday, so supper inevitably follows lunch. If your family eats breakfast with gusto and total fearlessness when it comes to starch and sugar, then they eat supper as though they're marching to the Ukraine as soon as they've finished their pudding and may not get another scrap of food until they get there. So there you are, with your steamed greens and slice of boiled chicken — and the special treat of a slice of crispbread and a bunch (small) of grapes — while they hoover in plates of sausage, chips and gravy (your husband and sons would eat pizza with gravy if you'd let them), mopping up any stray bits of grease, ketchup or sauce with blocks of bread. 'How's the chicken?' your husband asks in his kindly, husbandly way, as he pours another pint of gravy over his chips. You say, 'It's delicious, darling.' Your youngest son pretends to gag. 'Yuk,' he says, 'how can you eat spinach? It tastes like medicine.' 'It's not spinach,' you answer in a helpful, informative voice, a good mother is always teaching. 'It's greens.' At this news your older son belches. 'Ulk,' your older son mutters through a mouthful of sausage and potato. 'That's even worse.' 'You're not really fat, Mum,' says your lovely daughter. 'Why don't you just have a couple of potatoes? You love chips.' Her innocence almost brings tears to your eyes. You smile at her fondly as she wipes up eight hundred calories of drippings with a thick slice of buttered bread. If you don't either starve or binge yourself to death beforehand, in a year or two she will be sitting there beside you with the same cup and a half of limp turnip tops and the same bald slice of chicken as you, worrying that everybody at school calls her chubby and that she's got a spot coming. 'No, no, dear,' you say, 'I'm really enjoying this. It's *so* healthy.' You hold up a forkful of what to the unpracticed eye looks like what Rollo pukes up when he's been eating grass. 'I can't tell you how delicious this is,' you say (this statement at least is true). 'I don't see why you can't have just a couple of chips,' says your daughter. You shove the greens into your mouth before you can say, 'Well, you will.'

And then, at last, supper is over. Your husband goes to read the paper. Your children go off to pretend to do their homework. Rollo falls asleep. You are alone in the kitchen. Or not quite alone. There are some cold, soggy chips in the serving dish. Your youngest son has left half a sausage in congealed gravy on his plate. Your oldest son has left sixteen peas and a half a slice of bread. There are some fried onions still in the pan. There are three chips on your daughter's plate. They polished off the litre of ice cream but they left three biscuits. 'Feed me!' rumbles your stomach.

'Feed me! Feed me!' You look at the sink. You look out the window. You turn to the sign taped to the fridge: WHY ARE YOU OPENING THIS DOOR? THINK BEFORE YOU EAT! And then you:

a. pop the last of your twelve allotted grapes into your mouth and start to wash up.

b. scrape everything, including the untouched biscuits, into the bin. You poke the bread and the biscuits as far down as you can with the handle of a serving spoon. You throw the oil from the potatoes over them. You stare at the empty boxes and jars, the potato peelings, the tea leaves and coffee grounds and dried-up blobs of dog food, but what you see is the sweet face of your daughter holding up a perfect, golden chip and saying, 'Go on, Mum, you're not *really* fat,' Your husband looks up, bemused, as you rush out of the house with the rubbish in your arms.

c. eat the peas. No sooner has the last pea fallen hollowly into your stomach than you feel your body put on three new pounds. 'Don't do this,' you tell yourself. 'Whatever you do, don't do this.' You eat one biscuit, but manage to throw the other two into the chip pan. 'Stop now,' you advise yourself. 'If you stop now it won't be so bad.' But you don't stop. You eat half of the remains of the sausage, and then rudely wake up Rollo to stuff the other half into his mouth. 'Okay,' you say. 'Okay, you're still ahead of the game. You may be 253 calories over your daily allowance. It's not a disaster. If you skip the skinny girl's breakfast tomorrow and take Rollo for a three-mile run before lunch, you'll not only make up for this *and* work off at least a quarter of a pound, you'll be too tired to eat your cheese and apple for lunch.' With a strength and fortitude your warrior forebears would have been proud of, you scrape everything in sight that is edible even by the most liberal standards into Rollo's dish. You will deal with the vet's lecture about overfeeding corgis and their little hearts having to overwork when the time comes.

d. grip the edge of the sink. You open the cupboard, on the inside door of which you have taped a photograph of Cher in a G-string and a few rhinestones. Over this picture you have written: This Could Be You. You stare at it. 'This could never be you,' says a tiny, treacherous voice inside you; a voice that is craving a cold, fat-soaked chip. 'Look at her. Go on, take a good look. She has no grey hair. She has no crows' feet. She has no circles under her eyes. Her face isn't crumbling. She only has one chin. Where you're hippy she has a bone. Who are you kidding?' So, okay you say to yourself, so I'll never be Cher. That's not so bad. At least I don't wake up whimpering in the middle of the night because I was once married to Sonny Bono. Even a ten-inch waist doesn't truly compensate a person for that. But that treacherous little voice hasn't shut up yet. 'So why fight it?' it whispers. 'Why go on torturing yourself? Why spend some of the best years of your life watching everyone else in the world eating and drinking and being merry while you chew your carrot sticks twenty-three times and dream about drowning in mashed potatoes? Why not have a little fun? Why not enjoy yourself for a change? There's plenty of time to be skinny when you're dead.' You pour yourself a litre of water and drink it down. There, you think, that's better. But this voice isn't giving up so easily. A couple of gallons of water, a five-mile run, even a whole head of lettuce stuffed into your mouth by the handful isn't going to deter it. Chances are that even if you were to get your mind off food by making wild, passionate love to Harrison Ford, the second you squelched apart, your breathing laboured, this same little voice would start shouting, 'Okay, okay, that was nice, but what's there to eat?' Now it says, 'One chip, no gravy, and a spoonful of peas.' You stare at the cold-water tap. 'No,' you say. 'You only live once,' screams the voice. 'You're not going to be reincarnated as a burger chef with a hyperactive thyroid, you know. This is it. That chip will never come your way again.' So you eat one chip. . . .

e. you think that if you start with the half a sausage in the congealed gravy it will be so disgusting that you won't want to eat anything else, not even the biscuits, and certainly not those soggy chips. But you are wrong.

12. The family and a few close friends are sitting in the living room, watching a video. On the coffee table in the centre of this circle is a plate of biscuits everyone was too full from dinner to eat as dessert. When the movie is over and the lights come on, of the two dozen biscuits that were on the plate when the lights first went out there are seven survivors. What happens next?

a. You ask everyone if they'd like some tea.

b. You spirit the biscuit plate into the kitchen while everyone else is still saying, 'What do you think that dream sequence in the middle was meant to be about?' Then you put some more biscuits on it and bring it back out with the tea.

c. Your husband says, 'What happened to all the biscuits?' One of your least favourite sons sniggers. You say, cool as a woman who has just robbed the local bank and returned home to have supper with the police, 'Would anyone care for a cup of tea?'

d. You turn to your nearest offspring. 'Jasper, for God's sake! You've eaten all the biscuits!' 'What a pig,' chimes in Jasper's sister. 'Oink-oinkoinkoinkoink.' Jasper, looking injured, whines, 'I did not, I only had *one*!', but no one hears him because at that very moment, as luck would have it, you are taking orders for tea.

e. Your children all shout, 'Which greedy pig ate all the chocolate chip cookies? We didn't get any!' You look stern and say, 'Oh for goodness sake, grow up, will you?'

13. You're alone in the house. It's a windy, rainy night. There's a great film on television, one you've been looking forward to seeing. You pour yourself a glass of white wine (everyone knows that red is fattening). You put the bottle back in the fridge and stand there, gazing in. Then, as the advert ends and the voice of the television begins to announce the start of the film, you:

a. grab the cheese and olives and the tub of humus, shut the door, balance your glass on top of the humus, and head for the sofa.

b. hesitate. What's a glass of wine without an olive? Without a tiny piece of cheese? But are we talking 'an' olive here? Are we speaking in terms of one small piece of cheese or half a wheel? The wind howls through the trees. The rain beats against the pane. The announcer says, 'a classic of its kind'. You slam the refrigerator door shut, whisk the bag of crunchy crinkle-cut crisps out of the cupboard, and charge into the living room, upsetting the cat.

c. slam the fridge shut. The windows rattle. When you were a kid you used to love to sit up in bed on stormy nights, reading mysteries and eating sweets and homemade biscuits. Those were some of the happiest times of your life. With one last look at the restless night, you activate the alarm on the fridge. If now your resolve should weaken and you should sneak back in during a commercial break for something to munch on, your son's heavy metal band singing a special rendition of 'What Kind of Fool Am I?' (*What kind of fool am I, who always eats too much, it seems that food's the only thing that I have been thinking of....*) will be heard through the land. It will certainly be heard through the land immediately surrounding you — by the people upstairs, the people next door, and the beautiful, skinny blonde at the back.

d. say, 'I could have a couple of olives, for heaven's sake, Or a few nuts even. Nuts are healthy.' Then you say, 'No. If I have a couple of olives I'll want some cheese to go with them.' 'Of course, cheese is good for you, too.' 'Yes, but who can eat cheese without biscuits?' 'Crispbread?' you further ask. 'Crispbread tastes like cardboard and has fewer calories.' 'Maybe I should just have a handful of nuts.' 'But to have a handful of nuts I have to open the pound box of nuts. If I open the pound box of nuts I'll eat the whole thing. Then I'll feel sick and disgusted with myself.' 'But maybe I won't eat the whole thing. I mean, nobody's making me eat an entire pound of peanuts, are they? Nobody's standing over me with a gun, saying, "Lady, you better eat every nut in that container, even the little shrivelled ones." Why don't I just weigh out two ounces of peanuts and eat them very slowly, one at a time? Then I'll feel pretty good about myself. I'll feel that I've achieved something.' 'But what about the cheese and biscuits? If I had two ounces of nuts I could also have two ounces of cheese and three or four pieces of crispbread. I didn't have breakfast. I had two apples for lunch. That's nothing. Recent medical evidence suggests that not eating is as bad as eating. It messes up your metabolism. I don't want to mess up my metabolism.' 'No, but on the other hand I don't want to gain five pounds just watching a two-hour movie.' 'There's some mango chutney hidden in the old short-bread tin under the sink. I really love cheese with mango chutney.' 'Mango chutney, cheese, biscuits, and nuts? Are you completely out of your mind or something? What is this, the lost weekend? What is this, suicide by protein and fibre?' 'But it's raining,' you say. You turn towards the window. It is raining.

e. stand there for so long that not only has the voice of the television explained what a wonderful film you're about to watch, the wonderful film has already started. Leaving the fridge ajar, you race into the living room, unplug the set and carry it into the kitchen. So you can watch the show and decide how many olives you're going to eat at the same time.

14. You're on holiday. You and your family have rented a house on the Java Sea with a friend and her family. And it is beautiful! Was it worth the expensive airfare and the long, boring flight with some stewardess shoving a plate of boiled chicken under your nose every three hours. This is paradise! This is the holiday of a lifetime! Your husband and you are carrying on

like honeymooners. Your friend and you have never laughed so much. Even the children are having a fantastic time, and are behaving as though they may someday turn into people and as though they are, for a change, happy not to have been born into another family. Your husband and you walk along the beach in the moonlight, listening to the waves kiss the shore and watching the water shimmer with luminous fish, and you say to each other, 'Darling, this is an experience to treasure and remember for as long as we live.' The next day you are all sitting on the beach, sipping refreshing tropical drinks as you bask in the sunshine, when someone pulls out a camera. 'Come on!' they cry. 'Come on! Time to take some precious photographs to record this idyllic time for ever and ever.' You:

a. say, 'Great idea!' and smile directly into the lens.

b. never let anyone take a photograph of you in beachwear. Not with those knees. Not with those upper arms. Not with Nivea on your nose. You pull a small child in front of you (you are sitting sort of hunched up on the blanket) just as the camera goes click.

c. have never had a decent photograph taken of yourself since you were six months old. Other people may try to argue that you look perfectly fine in that snapshot where you look like a bowling pin but you know better. Other people may say you're actually quite photogenic but you know that what you are is the type of person who gets in front of a camera and immediately looks like either a criminal or a zombie — and a criminal or a zombie with a weight problem at that. As soon as you see that little black box being lifted out of that beach bag you scream, 'Toilet!' and race towards the house (where you will stay until you're sure the film has run out).

d. have had several arguments with your beloved, over the years, about your fear of celluloid (as opposed to what he considers to be your irrational terror of cellulite). But it has never made you feel any better that every time you say, 'I don't look like me in pictures,' he says, 'Yes you do, dear.' Quite the opposite, in fact. In the family photo album the only pictures of you are one where you're peaking out of a cutout of a bathing beauty on Brighton Pier (he was standing too far away and he got the focus wrong so that, in fact, it might not even be you as far as anyone can tell) and your wedding photograph (even you couldn't cut yourself out of that one). You can tell from the way he gripped your wrist the second the camera was produced that he is not going to let you get out of having your picture taken this time. So you don't even struggle. You don't say one word about what you look like in a swimsuit or how your hair looks like you slept in it. You stand up beside him, wrap your arms around him, and smile as Bo Derek would when confronted with a precision lens. Later, while everyone is splashing in the water, you accidentally open the back of the camera. You do, of course, close it again immediately, but chances are that steady tropical sun has ruined the film. Oh dear.

e. have your picture taken on the beach. You have your picture taken under palm trees. You have your picture taken on the terrace. You have your picture taken in shorts, swimsuits, and sundresses. You even have your picture taken with an ice cream in your hand. When you get home and the sixteen rolls of film have been developed you sit with your loved ones reliving each magic moment. 'Remember that?' 'Wasn't that wonderful?' 'Look at Mum! She looks like she's got something stuffed in her cheeks.' You laugh, you oh, you ah, you remember. And as soon as everyone's asleep, you tiptoe downstairs and burn every photograph of you under the grill.

15. Oh, no, it's Halloween again. And this year you've been invited to a fancy dress party. It might not have caused the immediate reaction, 'Oh my God, the fancy dress party at the end of the universe!' had the theme been Cuddly Toys or Monsters of Song, Films and Literature. But it's not. It's Arabian Nights. What are the chances that any woman with a fair to stupendous figure is going to go as anything other than a belly dancer? About one in a million. You, though cute in your way and the love object of a wonderful human being, do not have a stupendous figure, despite the fact that you have been on a diet for more years

than you were not on a diet. Your wonderful human being is going to go to this party, whether you go or not. What do you do? You can't set him loose in a semi-detached house with thirty beautiful women wearing satin bras and glass rubies in their navels. But you can't don the veils and hip-huggers yourself. What are you supposed to go as, a camel? In the end you:

a. go as a stuffed aubergine — and win the Most Original Costume prize, as well as the attention of every sheik and eunuch in the house.

b. go as a belly dancer, but refuse to take your coat off. This doesn't make you as conspicuous as it might, since there are at least seven other belly dancers at this party still in their anoraks or duffle coats. While the belly dancers with the hour-glass figures all wiggle from the bar to the buffet table to the dance floor, knocking back the beer and peanuts and showing off their rubies, you and the belly dancers who feel the cold huddle in one corner, keeping your eyes on your thieves and princes and comparing dieting notes.

c. go as a camel. As the end of the camel, in fact. This means that you get to keep a close eye on the whereabouts of your wonderful human being at all times and don't have an opportunity to eat too many falafels or too much Turkish delight. Even better, though, it means you don't have to spend the evening wishing a giant genie would appear and spirit all the belly dancers away to some place where there are no men, it's colder than Iceland in the winter, there are no spare coats for them, and from which they can never return — that sort of wishing, you know from experience, creates frown lines and makes a girl hungry.

b. get a crippling migraine three hours before the party. Your wonderful person goes off on his own. He can't be all that wonderful, can he? If he were really all that wonderful, he'd stay home and nurse you instead of getting into his white robe and wrapping a tablecloth around his head. For the first hour that he's gone you watch television. For the second hour you eat everything in the fridge that doesn't look as though it might bite back. In the third hour you have to go out to the all-night petrol station to buy more food. By the time he comes home you aren't speaking to him. But you won't tell him why.

e. you go as a First Wife. First Wives, you know from your extensive knowledge of Hollywood films, don't have to bare their tummies to a critical assemblage of anorexics and though they tend not to be as sexually attractive as the other harem girls, they are usually held in high esteem by the sheik himself because of their wisdom, experience and good sense of humour. The sheiks at this party, though, seem to have a total disregard for wise and witty First Wives well wrapped up in robes and veils. They're all hanging around the skimpily clad harem girls, who, of all things, have sewn coins on their bra straps so that when they dance (which they do at every possible opportunity, whether there is music or not), they jangle in a really childish way. Even the sheik who unstops your drains the rest of the year is hanging around with a blonde belly dancer who laughs in much the way that a horse farts. You and the other First Wives gather around the crisp bowl and brood. By the time you get home you aren't speaking to your wonderful person. You won't tell him why. You sit up long after he's gone to bed, eating the half of Halloween cake left in the fridge.

Scoring

Give yourself zero points for every a answer; and five points for every other answer. Yes, that's right: five points for each b, c, d, or e. Did you think no one would notice? This isn't like eating a malt loaf after your slice of lettuce and one ounce of tuna in brine, you know. You can't just flush the wrapper down the loo and act like it never happened.

If you score a total of zero you are a chirpy, if chunky, normal person, with a lot of self-respect and a cavalier attitude towards the whims and demands of the fascistic fashion conspiracy. 'I'm me!' you say every time you look in the mirror. 'And that's not only great, it's all that counts.' Jane bets you've never won any beauty contests. To which you, of course, reply, 'You bet your tummy tucks I haven't. I'd rather spend three weeks on Islay counting the sheep than be in a beauty contest. I wouldn't be caught dead parading around in a swimsuit and a sash while a bunch of brain-dead boneheads sit at home watching television, slugging back the beer and catching peanuts in their mouths and saying, 'Whoowhoo-whoo, look at the tits on that one!' Jane says it's clear to her that nobody would want you in a beauty contest, dead or otherwise.

If you score thirty or below, you are a real person in the body of someone who is tyrannized by the spectre of body fat and physical imperfections. You're what is known as a victim of your times. The real person in you is struggling to make herself heard and seen, but the way you respond to the sight of a double decker sandwich on your plate, or a full-length mirror anywhere in your vicinity, is still much the way those poor dogs responded to that bloody bell: you still do exactly what you've been taught to do far more often than you say to yourself, 'If I just dig my way out of here I won't have to depend on that stupid bell and that idiot who rings it.'

A score of thirty-five or over indicates a person stepping through life as a soldier through a mine-field. Everything is out to get you. The kindly friend who brings you a cake for your birthday; the mother whose poor skin you inherit; the father who gave you the build of a brown bear; the sister who can eat six meals a day, plus desserts, and never gain a gram; the corner shop, the invitation to dinner, the newsagent's. You have been told, subtlely and cleverly, that fat is the same as ugly, and that ugly is the same as bad, worthless and doomed to be lonely. And you believe it. You live in terror of the thick eyebrow and the heavy ankle. If you were to run into Frank Zappa in the shopping centre and he were to ask you, 'Hey, lady, what's the ugliest part of your body?' you would go pale and start to shake. Was he referring to your stubby fingers? Your bitten nails? Your hips? You'd be standing there, beneath the harsh flourescent lights of a major department store, trying to hide every bit of your body and still be polite. You'd smile (but not so much that he could catch a glimpse of those incisors). 'What?' you'd ask, holding back the tears and steadying yourself on a table of cycling shorts. 'You heard me,' Frank would say in that candid, no-bullshit way of his. 'What's the ugliest part of your body?' You'd sort of tilt into the stretch tops. What *did* he mean? Your hairy arms? Your long bony neck? Your beady eyes? Your thin, mud-coloured tresses? Had he somehow heard about your shinbone or your spotty bum? Had someone told him about your ears? Had your sister been spreading rumours about your feet again? It would never occur to you that he didn't mean your nose. Finally, when he'd realized that you weren't about to answer his question, Frank would sing, 'I think it's your mind.' You'd be sure you hadn't heard him correctly. 'My mind?' you'd repeat. 'Uh huh,' Frank would smile. 'Your mind.' You'd start laughing. You'd stop hugging your coat to your body and hunching into your collar to obscure your chin and your neck, and you'd throw your arms around him. 'My mind!' you'd cry. 'What a relief!'

'Oh, for heaven's sake, Serena,' says Jane. 'What are you banging on about? There's nothing wrong with a person being concerned about her appearance. I happen to know for a fact that you didn't come out of the house at all in June 1986 because of your hair.'

So?

'And who drove down to Charing Cross in the middle of the night to leave boxes of food out for the homeless?'

Are you insinuating that that wasn't a charitable work?

'Charitable work my lash curlers. That was to get rid of all the food that was left from your birthday party so you wouldn't eat it yourself for breakfast.'

Well, it worked, didn't it?

Jane huffs. She says she doesn't see what I think I've proven with this quiz. That it's wrong to want to look nice? That you're crazy or something if you don't want to be fat? That she, Jane Marigold Forbes-Smythe, should be held up to public ridicule simply because she once turned down a date with Richard E. Grant on the grounds that she was on a diet and he wanted to take her out to eat? 'You know what it's like when you've come through eleven whole days without once hitting cheese and onion crisps and sour cream dip,' says Jane. 'I wouldn't have stood a chance. Once I got started it would have been dangerous for him to put his fork down while he sipped his wine. I'd have had his plate cleared in a matter of seconds.'

That's exactly what I think I've proven.

'What is?'

That those of us on a permanent diet not only have an irrational and unreal attitude about our bodies, but the way we deal with what we see as our weight problem and the threat food poses to us is irrational and unreal as well.

'It's not.'
How about one more quiz?
'Is this going to be like just one more crisp?'
It wouldn't surprise me.

5.

Food and You:
The Second Quizzes

Simply fill in the blanks in the sentences that follow with the appropriate response.

1. I _____ talk to my food.
   a. always
   b. never
   c. sometimes

2. When I talk to my food, I _____ say something like, 'This is going to be good,' or. 'Wow, isn't this delicious? Food, I love you!'
   a. never
   b. always
   c. sometimes

3. When I talk to my food, I _____ say something like, 'My hips aren't going to thank me for this,' or 'I'm really going to regret this tomorrow.'
   a. always
   b. never
   c. sometimes

4. After I've eaten something — be it an apple or a deep-fried kebab — I _____ say: 'I feel fat.'
   a. always
   b. never
   c. sometimes

5. I _____ ask people if my bum's too big.
   a. always
   b. never
   c. sometimes

6. If I have, in passing, asked someone if they think my bum is too big, I _____ believe them if they say no.
   a. never
   b. naturally
   c. want to

7. If I were casually to drop into conversation my doubts as to the size of my bum or the consistency of my thighs and the person asked were to say, 'Well, to be honest, Pandora, that is not a small bottom we're talking about here,' or 'Let's face it, lovey, if you were a cow you'd never have any hope of turning up as "lean" mince,' I _____ upset.
   a. would be very
   b. would not be
   c. would be a little

8. In fact, if the person who told me I had a fat bum or wobbly thighs was my husband or boyfriend I would be very likely to _____
   a. burst into tears, throw something at him, and not speak to him for at least three days.
   b. ask him to explain himself, e.g. is he making a pass — I want to feel that gorgeous fat bum of yours wiggling against me — or is he upset because he doesn't understand the programme we're watching about quantum mechanics and needs something simple to say?
   c. ignore him.

9. I _____ spend a lot of time worrying about how I look.
   a. do
   b. do not
   c. suppose I do

10. By 'a lot' I mean _____
    a. every waking hour, even when I'm supposed to be worrying about my speech for Friends of the Earth or my meeting with the Prime Minister.
    b. whenever I'm going to be on television or giving a speech to more than six hundred people.
    c. whenever I see someone who is prettier or thinner than I am.

11. By 'worry' I mean _____
    a. I think seriously about liposuction and plastic surgery.
    b. I think, perhaps I should wear something that's clean and doesn't have any visible holes.
    c. I stop eating for a day or two, or have my hair cut, or eat a jar of peanut butter while standing at the sink.

12. I weigh myself _____
    a. twice a day.
    b. when I'm pregnant.
    c. once a day, but I don't look.

13. I _____ eat one crisp and leave the rest of the packet.
    a. wouldn't even try to
    b. can
    c. haven't yet been able to

14. I _____ on a crash diet.
    a. am always
    b. have never been
    c. have been

15. By 'crash' I mean _____
    a. I eat under eight hundred calories for several days and then I eat a large cheese and mushroom pizza, garlic bread and drink three Diet Cokes by myself.
    b. I cut out all sweets and between-meal snacks and don't take seconds of anything but salad or steamed seaweed.
    c. I weigh or measure everything before I eat it. I don't eat anything with starch or sugar in it. I eat everything very slowly and chew it a lot. I don't go out or invite anyone over. The crash comes when I find myself standing at the fridge at two in the morning, eating a frozen fish finger.

16. I _____ hide food from myself.
    a. quite often
    b. would never think to
    c. have been known to

17. I hide it most often in _____
    a. the car (that way, if you suddenly decide you can't get through the night without a box of chocolates or a box of water biscuits and half a pound of cheddar, you have to put your coat on over your pyjamas and go out in the rain and risk being mistaken for a burglar.
    b. the highest shelf of the cupboard (like most people, I tend to forget pretty quickly about things that aren't at eye level).

c. the bathroom (that way you can run the shower while you eat and no one will suspect a thing).

18. Not being seen to eat is _____ not eating.
    a. the same as
    b. not at all like
    c. the next best thing to

19. I _____ get in moods where not even the mustard or the lime pickle are safe from me.
    a. often
    b. never
    c. sometimes

20. If I had a choice between being beautiful and winning the Nobel Peace Prize I would pick _____
    a. beautiful.
    b. the prize.
    c. beautiful, as long as my looks weren't going to start to go within the next five years.

21. If I had a choice between being skinny and happy I would pick _____
    a. skinny (it's the same thing, isn't it?).
    b. happy.
    c. skinny (it's easier to become happy if you're skinny than it is to become skinny if you're happy).

22. I have washed the mayonnaise out of the tuna salad _____
    a. (when I'd already had two sandwiches and was clearly going for a third and fourth).

   b. never (why on earth would you do a thing
      like that?).
   c. sometimes (but only, you know, if between
      making the tuna and lunch the next day I'd
      eaten half a lemon meringue and two boxes
      of Raisin Bran).

23. I _____ say, 'But that's fattening!'
   a. often
   b. never
   c. sometimes

24. I _____ clothes a size too small in order
   to bribe myself to stay on my diet.
   a. frequently buy
   b. have never even thought of buying
   c. once or twice have bought

SCORING

An a gets you three points, b gets you one, c gets you
two.

If you emerged with between twenty-four and
thirty-six points you have a healthy working relationship with your body, with no more than the
sort of concerns about fatty tissue and public
image that anyone might have.

Between thirty-six and forty-eight you and your
body still get along, but you're becoming a little
more concerned about it than may be actually
good for you.

Forty-eight to sixty? You should try to think of
something other than your body now and then.

Over sixty? If you managed to think of something

other than your body, if you managed, for instance, to think about the Greenhouse Effect, your next thought would be sure to be something like, 'My God, is that going to dry out my skin?'

Which of the following statements is true about you?

1. I could stand to lose a few pounds.

2. My hips could stand to lose a few pounds.

3. If it weren't for my elbows my body wouldn't be too bad.

4. If it weren't for my nose my face would be perfect.

5. I have the same reaction to suddenly coming upon a mirror as a vampire.

6. I'm going on a diet tomorrow.

7. I'm on a diet now.

8. I know the calorie value, fat content and carbohydrate count of most foods, including different brand items.

9. I have a recurring dream that I meet Bruce Springsteen at a party. He likes me. We talk and talk and talk. And then we dance. He's a great dancer. He says I'm a great dancer. We go to his place for a nightcap. One thing leads to another. He begs me to make love with him. He's got that cute smile and he's so sincere ... who could resist? But just as I'm slipping off my jeans he bangs into something and,

screaming with pain, turns on the light so he can see if he's cut badly or not. I'm trapped in the 300-watt glare of the overhead lamp, with my jeans around my ankles and my cellulite and stretchmarks in plain view. I hop from the room while he's still trying to staunch the bleeding, pull my clothes back on and, carrying my shoes, run outside and hail a cab.

10. I once threw out a dozen brownies and then went back a few hours later, scraped the tea leaves off them, and ate every one.

11. I hated myself for it.

12. Every time I take another crisp or another peanut or another piece of chocolate, I say, 'This is the last one.'

13. I never diet on Sundays.

14. I never diet when I'm on holiday.

15. I never diet when the moon is full.

16. Seeing other people eat a lot always makes me feel good.

17. Seeing other people eat a lot always makes me eat a lot (unless it's the first day of my crash diet, in which case it just makes me feel really good).

18. When I went to see that powerful, moving and provocative film about sexual obsession and manipulation, I was the only person who noticed that in the crucial scene where the heroine was telling the hero about her relationship with her father they walked past a café and that one of the couples in the cafe was

eating what had to be Texas chilli with flour tortillas and two kinds of salsa.

Scoring

The way I see it, if you answered 'true' to nine or less you are a lifetime dieter, but you're wishy washy. More than nine trues and you are a lifetime dieter of finesse and skill. And pretty obsessive.

'Oh, of course,' says Jane, 'as if any woman in her right mind would let Bruce Springsteen see her cellulite.'

Jane, Michelle Pfeiffer says that she scowls at beauty. She says she wouldn't recommend it to a single soul.

'Serena, if I looked like Michelle Pfeiffer that's what I'd say, too.'

Once again, extenuating circumstances such as 'I was very drunk at the time' or 'I'd just recovered from a long illness' are not permitted. Just a simple yes or no. Have you ever:

1. Eaten an entire box or bag of anything (cereal, crisps, cream-filled doughnuts)?
   And then put the bag in the dustbin of the people next door?

2. Come down to the kitchen in the morning and discovered a scene of carnage and devastation reminiscent of the Cimmerians' passage through the Kingdom of Van? Wrappers on the floor. Crumbs on the table. Jam jars that some

finger has scraped clean shoved deep into the bin. An empty bowl (that, when you went to bed, was still the home of the remains of last night's pasta salad) in the fridge beside the empty ploughman's pickle jar. Well, have you?

Did you blame the dog?

The kids?

Did you claim that you must have been sleep-walking?

3. Eaten everything the children left on their plates?

    Even what the toddler left?

    Even what the baby left?

4. Finished what everyone else couldn't eat in the restaurant, on the theory that you paid for it so you should eat it?

5. Deliberately broken your scales?

    More than once?

    On a regular basis?

6. Felt yourself driven to race around the corner in a blizzard to buy a large bar of chocolate (partly because eating when it's stormy outside is a comforting activity and partly because the fact that it is stormy means that it doesn't really count as a dieting day)?

    Even though it meant leaving the baby sleeping unattended for at least six minutes?

    Even though it meant waking up the baby, shoving its little snowsuit and woolly hat on and taking it outside in Arctic conditions?

    Did you get stricken with guilt halfway home and throw the chocolate into the first dustbin you came to?

When the baby's older brother came home from school and inquired as to why his sister's bunny snowsuit was sopping wet did you say you ran out of milk?

7. Owned a T-shirt that says: I CAN'T BE DEAD, I'M STILL ON A DIET?

Scoring

As far as I'm concerned, one 'yes' answer here is enough to suggest that when you have a bad day every mirror in the house is either covered over or hidden in the loft. And that on a really bad day there isn't a dry cracker in the house that is safe from you. Even the baby better keep an eye on her stewed marrow.

Jane scowls. 'Get real, Serena,' says Jane. 'You could be describing anyone.'

Match the words in List A with the definitions in List B. It is possible that some words might fit more than one definition; and some definitions might fit more than one word.

List A

a. eat
b. is she thin?
c. none
d. one of anything
e. Sunday
f. having your jaw wired
g. starvation

h. a miracle
i. chocolate
j. tomorrow
k. yesterday
l. her weight
m. almost anything
n. never
o. diet books
p. your birthday
q. for you, nothing
r. your mother
s. you don't
t. an empty box of biscuits
u. two empty boxes of biscuits
v. a shoebox full of chocolate bars, crisps, and packets of cakes and biscuits
w. fat
x. hungry
y. liposuction
z. except for my bum/nose/eyes/feet/neck/skin/knees/teeth/lips/eyelashes

List B

1. The first thing you notice about anyone.
2. A day on which no one diets.
3. The one thing that you know will make you thin once and for all.
4. The day you went on your first diet.
5. Something you do when you're hungry.
6. The day you will go on your next diet.
7. The most important thing in anyone's life.
8. What every lifetime dieter has in her wardrobe.
9. I think that I'm attractive.
10. What you do when you're not hungry.

11. What you do when you're not on a diet.
12. Something every lifetime dieter has in her cupboard.
13. Something every lifetime dieter has too much of.
14. What you always feel.
15. The first question you ask when you find out your boyfriend is seeing someone else.
16. How much you have to eat to gain weight.
17. Something it is impossible to eat.
18. The reason you can have that hot fudge sundae even though you're on a diet.
19. Something that is far far worse than being fat.
20. What you can always be today that you weren't yesterday.

Scoring

Actually, the matching quiz isn't for scoring. There aren't any answers that are more right or wrong than others. It's more of a summary personal profile, if you like. Compare your results with those of a friend. Have a discussion.

'I'd like to discuss a couple of things, Serena,' says Jane.

You would?

'Yes, I would.'

What would you like to discuss?

'I'd like to discuss the fact that I still don't know what you're trying to say.'

I'm trying to say that women are caught on the horns of a dilemma. And pretty big horns they are, too.

'The horns of a dilemma?'

Think about it.

When she's a child, a person is taught that food is good for her. It nourishes. It supports life. Having enough food to eat, moreover, is a sign of prosperity and wellbeing. 'Clean your plate!' says her mother. 'You can't leave this table till you've eaten every spoonful,' says her father. They remind her about all the children in the world who would give anything (had they anything) to have the bowl of bean stew towards which she holds such a negative attitude. And when she's a child, she is also taught that it is women who are the nurturers. To say 'woman' is to say 'comfort, nourishment, food'; to say 'mother' is to say 'fudge brownies'.

But then, she becomes a woman — and all of a sudden everything's changed. They were lying to her all along! Food isn't good for you, it's bad. Women may nurture but the only thing they'd better consume are cosmetics, clothes, jewellery, perfumes, and diet pills. Mothers may spend their lives up to their elbows in bangers and mash, but a woman who is sexually attractive grows faint at the sight of a crumpet, jumps back in horror when approached by spaghetti. Her mother starts saying pointed things like, 'I wouldn't wear those shorts out in public if I were you, sweetie.' Her father is overheard telling her mother that he's worried they'll never find anyone to marry her if she doesn't cut back on the sweets. And then, even though she doesn't exactly have the figure of a plank of wood, she finds a man who truly loves her — and what does he say? He says, 'Darling, you're getting a bit of a bum, you know.' He says, 'Women aren't meant to have tummies, Pandora. They're meant to be flat.' He says, 'In all honesty, love of my life, I'll leave you if you ever get fat.'

The horns are out. She can't open a magazine or a

newspaper, turn on the television or go to a film, without being bombarded by images of two things: 1. food; and 2. thin, beautiful young women (usually not fully dressed). 'Eat! Eat! Eat!' screams the world. 'Come on, sister, pack it in!' But at the same time, of course, it is saying, 'Whatever you do, don't eat! Whatever you do, don't even let your body look as though you enjoy your food! It's better to be drop-dead gorgeous than smart or of sterling character,' the world informs you. 'Have your stomach stapled if you must!'

This is what is known as a double bind. You're damned if you do and you're damned if you don't. You could win if you had a tapeworm, maybe, or a family of amoebas living in your intestines, but under normal conditions it isn't easy. You are encouraged to eat because it's fun, to eat because it's comforting, to eat when you watch a movie or watch television or are on a long journey, whether you're hungry or not, and then you are told that eating makes you un-attractive. So what do you do? So you do both.

You summon all your strength and will power into one room and you say, 'Okay, guys, this is it. We're on a diet.' Strength and will power, who figure they were designed for more important things than keeping you out of the biscuit section of Sainsbury's, look at each other and roll their eyes. Here we go again, their expressions say. 'I want total control,' you tell them. 'I don't want to be a plaything of my tastebuds. I don't want to be at the mercy of my olfactory organs. So they dig in their heels. No snacks between meals. No double portions. Nothing fried or sauced or creamed or buttered. No meals worth mentioning.

And then you have a bad day. Or you're blue. Or you're lonely. Or you're really really hungry (it happens). Or you're angry. In the normal way of things, if you were feeling low, you might treat yourself to an ice cream or a bag of dry-roasted peanuts or a bowl of chicken soup when you need a little cosmic hugging. In the normal way of things, you might throw something at the cat or clean the bathroom if you were mad at someone. But the normal way of things does not operate here. 'I'm going to eat!' you scream. 'Just try to stop me.' 'I'll show that rotten bum!' you roar. 'I'll get even with him ....' Your strength and will power start beeping and flashing. 'NO! NO! NO! NO! YOU'RE NOT ALLOWED!' And because you're not allowed, once you start you can't stop. Strength and will power are doing their nuts, but you, as guilty after one fruit gum as you will be after a large portion of chips and a potato fritter, steam on.

It is an example of the little ironies with which life likes to keep itself amused, that once a person has accepted the idea that a woman should have a fantastic body and be orgasmically beautiful or she might as well be on the moon, she can only fail. Either she doesn't have a fantastic body and isn't orgasmically beautiful, and, like the aardvark, was never intended to have such or be so, and ends up wasting precious years of her life trying to make herself into something she's not. Or she does have a great body and the sort of looks that reputedly launch ships, and then has to devote all her energies to making sure that she keeps them for as long as possible — if not longer.

'So now what are you saying?' asks Jane.

I'm saying that life's a bitch.

'Oh great,' says Jane. 'Well, I know what happens next, of course. Life's a bitch....'

And then you diet.

PART TWO

... AND THEN YOU DIET

6.

'Most Women Are a Diet Just Waiting to Happen' (or Starting Your Diet)

One day, when I was young and idealistic, I announced that I was never going to go on a diet again as long as I lived. I made this announcement at a family dinner. It was brought on by a comment of my sister's that she was surprised I wasn't weighing out the meal on my portable scale. 'My God, Serena!' exclaimed my sister. 'Are you ill or something? You're not weighing the salt.'

'No more,' said I. 'I can see now that I have been ridiculous. I can see now that I was becoming pathologically obsessive. From this day on I'm going to eat normal meals like a normal person.'

My mother said, 'That's wonderful, dear.' She turned to my father. 'Isn't that wonderful, John?'

John said, 'Does that mean I'll be able to eat a dish of ice cream again without causing a revolution? Does that mean we don't have to sneak the chocolate digestives in secret anymore?' He speared a chunk of cauliflower cheese. 'My God!' he cried. 'Does this mean the rest of us will be allowed to eat bread and butter in public again?'

'Eat what you want,' I smiled. 'I will. I'm throwing away my calorie counter. I'm throwing away my sixteen diet books. I'm selling my exercise machine.... I'm liberated! I'm free at last!' I laughed, scooping up a forkful of apple sauce and putting it into my mouth without so much as a single, momentary wonder as to whether it was one tablespoon or two, sweetened or un-. 'I am no longer going to be tyrannized by the idea of skinny. So what if I have hips? So what if there is no part of my anatomy that looks like a floor? I like my body. My body and I are pals. You don't starve your pal, do you? You don't deny your pal everything she loves just so you can wear a size eight mini.' I helped myself to gravy.

'And what brought on this change?' asked my sister, whose solution to dieting was simply to fast three days a week.

I waggled a chicken leg in her direction. 'I just suddenly realized that dieting makes me miserable. I'm unhappy, I'm grumpy, and I'm so terrified of eating that I do nothing all day but think about food.' I dipped the drumstick in gravy. 'And now I feel great!'

My sister said, 'Um.'

My mother said, 'I don't mind telling you that I got a little worried when you said you thought that cucumbers were fattening.'

My father said, 'I can't believe it, I can eat again in my own house without feeling like a criminal.'

My grandmother, Sadie, who now and then says something worth remembering, and even quoting, said something worth remembering and even quoting then. 'It won't last,' said Sadie, holding out her wine-glass for a refill. 'There's hardly a woman in the world who isn't a diet just waiting to happen.'

My mother looked at her. My sister looked at her. I looked at her. Her words shimmered in the air above the roast chicken and the cauliflower and the mashed potatoes — above us. A woman is a diet just waiting to happen. My father laughed.

Were truer words ever spoken? Though Sadie might, of course, have amended them slightly. She might have said, 'There's hardly a woman in the world who isn't a diet just waiting to happen — again and again and again and again.' She might have added, 'You'll lose count.'

Deciding to Go on a Diet

Just as a person never forgets her first period, the first time she shaved her legs, her first boyfriend, her first kiss, or the very first time she ever made love, she always remembers her first diet. There she was, munching away on a packet of Gypsy Creams, when she saw those words emblazoned across the page of that glossy magazine: Ten Easy Days to a Slimmer You. Beneath them was a thin, supple body in a pink leotard, apples and celery sticks floating around her. She remembers thinking to herself, do I look like that? She remembers standing on the edge of the bath to see more than her forehead in the mirror. She didn't look like that. She remembers making that very first dieter's shopping list: cottage cheese, carrots, celery, apples, tomato juice, crispbread, stock cubes. She savours the memory of waking up on that sunny morning and shouting to the sky, 'I start my diet today!' Oh the heady excitement of sitting down to a breakfast of half a grapefruit and a slice of dry toast! Oh the thrill of those first two carrot sticks and a six-ounce glass of tomato juice at eleven!

But does she remember her fourth diet? Her tenth diet? Her forty-first? No more than she remembers her fourth kiss, or her tenth boyfriend (was he the one with the nose or the one with the car you had to crank?), or her forty-first tussle with her diaphragm.

Does she know, by any chance, how any of those diets began? What event it was — large or small, catastrophic or trivial — that made her get her skipping rope out of the cupboard under the stairs, and her scales down from the loft? She may know without a doubt that she started her first diet because Penny Winterscoop, the most popular girl in the fifth year, had the generosity of spirit to tell her that if she had her fat legs she'd saw them off, but God alone knows why she went on the kiwi fruit diet, or the water diet, or the diet that led to her buying a dog (so she'd have some company on those twelve-mile walks she had to take before every meal).

Dieting is like any other addiction. Once you've had that first drink or that first hit, everything about the next drink or the next hit is all settled but the date and time. Once you've been on your first diet, the urge to go on one can come at any moment, in any place, and for any reason. You may go along for several months — even for a year or two — busy with other things, at peace or at least in a truce with your body, and then, all of a sudden, someone says something unkind about your legs, or you look in the mirror and don't like the face that's looking back at you, or you ask the sales assistant for a size ten in those satin jeans and when she stops cackling she says, 'For *you*?' It could be anything: the weather, UFO activity, having to wait for a train across from a six-foot poster of a leggy beauty in a T-shirt. Anything at all.

Here, for instance, is a possible scenario. Let's say that you haven't been on a diet since last May. And, on the whole, you've been feeling quite good about it. You tell your friends things like, 'I think my weight has stabilized. I feel comfortable, you know? All right, so maybe Cher isn't going to ask me for dieting tips, but I can live with that.' And then perhaps it's February. Perhaps it's February and, though a diet is the last thing on your mind, you've been feeling bored and restless since you made your last million, or Eric Clapton's been out of town so there's been no one to jam with lately. You decide to go shopping. 'I'll just look,' you say, as you set off. 'I'm not going to buy anything.' Three department stores later, you find yourself standing by a rack of dresses that were obviously designed with you in mind. 'That's me!' you cry excitedly to yourself. 'That is definitely me!' The only problem is that you do not come in One Size Fits All. You are cut so that the exact extent of a person's hips and bum matters. Whether you like it or not, you're going to have to try the dress on if you really want to buy it. You hold it up before you and its colours and contours whisper your name. The shoppers around you begin to mutter to one another, 'My God, that dress was made for her, wasn't it?' Oh yes, you definitely want it. So you head for the changing room.

But things are more informal, less private, than once they were. We, as people, are less inhibited and repressed. The changing room in this store is not a series of private cubicles, each with its own curtain or floor-to-ceiling door, as once it would have been. The changing room in this store is one large room, lined with several thousand mirrors and lit by several thousand bare 200-watt bulbs. The changing room in this store is filled with eat-your-heart-out-beautiful girls, all of whom have small flawless bodies and naturally blonde hair. To a woman, they turn the limpid pools they call their eyes on you. Their kiss-able mouths twitch in demure but recognizable smirks. You stand bravely at the entrance of the room for a second trying to decide what to do. Should you pretend that you just remembered you left the iron on? Should you just get undressed as unselfconsciously as they all have, ignoring the fact that, when you step out of your tracksuit, the first thought in the mind of every one of them is going to be, oh my God, I hope I don't ever look like that?'

'Oh come on,' you chide yourself, 'be an adult. These girls aren't interested in your puckered skin or jelly-like tummy. They're interested in getting into the tightest shorts and skimpiest tops they can find. They're not going to look at you.'

Your mother, who has given you similar talkings-to in the course of your relationship, would be proud of you as you march over to a corner and start slinging your things onto hooks. You stare into the mirror in front of you, but what you see is not you — sophisticated, intelligent, witty owner of a mature figure — but thirty-three bloody wood nymphs in bikinis, gazing at you in expectation.

To undress or not to undress, that is the question. whether it is a better idea to get out of your tracksuit and into the coveted garment as quickly as is humanly possible — taking into account that your sweatshirt may get stuck going over your head, or that you may have trouble getting the bottoms over your trainers, thus exposing your body to unlimited perusal. Or whether, instead, it would be a better idea to try to get the dress on without actually taking off anything else. You stare into the mirror some more. There is no way you can let these nymphs see your breasts or your wobbly upper arms, never mind anything else. The decision is made: you will pull the dress up. You wiggle out of the arms of your sweatshirt and then you climb into the frock. All goes well until it almost reaches hip level, that well-known danger zone. It can't get over your hips. Maybe it could get over your hips if they weren't clad in heavy, fleece-lined cotton, but it can't when they are.

You feel your face turning red. You break out in a cold sweat. You sort of shrug as though you're shrugging to yourself, 'Oh, ho hum, they just don't make sexy form-fitting sheaths like they used to, I suppose, maybe I won't bother trying it on after all.' You start to step back out of it. But there's a new problem. The zipper's caught on your tracksuit bottoms. You cast a surreptitious glance in the mirror before you. It's a sobering sight. One woman with the sort of figure a man can really get hold of, her hands sort of poking out from under an old sweatshirt, a shimmering orange confection bunched up over her grey sweatpants and, behind her, thirty-three girls with the sort of bodies men want to get hold of, their angelic faces and big blue eyes all focused on her. Truth, immutable and impersonal, makes itself known. You will never get the zipper unstuck unless you take off the bottoms. As you step out of the track suit, you're sure you hear one of the nymphs whisper to another, 'Oh my God, so that's what cellulite looks like. Disgusting!' And the other whisper back, 'Are *those* love handles? My God, she must be married to the Jolly Green Giant.'

Your next diet has just begun.

More or less.

The Day Before Your Diet Begins

'More or less?' asks the novice. 'What do you mean, more or less? Surely once you've decided to go on a diet, that's it. Good-bye egg salad sandwiches on thick brown bread with chips, and hello rice cakes and plain broth.'

Um, you'd think so, wouldn't you? But in this case, as in so many others in life, theory and practice often bear striking dissimilarities. Because before a person can officially start her diet she has to go through that time-honoured ritual known as The Day Before Your Diet Begins.

'The day before your diet begins?' inquires the novice politely. 'Is it important?'

Is it important? Is oxygen important? Is laughter important? Does the carbon cycle have a place in contemporary life?

Jane is emphatic. 'Yes,' she says, 'the day before you start your diet is important. In fact, psychologists now look on it as a kind of grief therapy.'

Grief therapy?

'Precisely. If your dog dies, you cry, don't you? You tell your friends all about the time Caesar got trapped in the dustbin and how you rescued him. You remind them of how cute he used to look when he was sleeping on their cashmere jackets. You sleep with his collar under your pillow. And in time you feel better. Right? Instead of bottling up your emotions, you've given them expression. Well that's therapeutic. That's good for you. It enables you to come to terms with Caesar's departure from your life. Your grief allows you to face the fact that you're never going to feel that little tongue in your ear at four in the morning again. The same process has to be gone through when you go on a diet. You have to say goodbye to the past. You have to separate yourself from the biscuit tin. You have to allow yourself to feel your bereavement at never having a Grolsch or a Piña Colada again, so long as you live, for a good long while.'

The novice looks puzzled. 'Grieve for your diet?'

'Really,' groans Jane. 'Of course not, stupid. You're not grieving *for* your diet. You're grieving for not not being on a diet.'

'Oh.' The novice clears her throat in a meditative

way. 'Well, exactly what form does this grief take?' she wants to know.

'You know,' says Jane. 'You eat everything in the house.'

'*Everything*?' repeats the novice.

'Well you're not going to be able to eat it the next day, are you?' asks Jane.

DIET EVE

A Play in One Act

SCENE ONE. Kitchen. Interior. Day. A fine grey light filters through the room. Outside, the birds squawk in the garden. The sound of low-flying aircraft can be heard overhead. Somewhere nearby someone is playing marching music. It is a typical Saturday morning in early spring. Two small figures sit around a wooden table. They are children, not gnomes. The little girl is shaking the last few flakes of corn from a large box of cereal. The little boy is doing something faintly disgusting with a banana and a glass of milk. It is a pleasant, family kitchen. There is a clock on the wall and socks drying on the radiator. There are letter magnets on the fridge spelling out the word DANGER! The little girl and the little boy, intent on their separate tasks, do not react immediately when a slightly plumpish woman in baggy trousers and a pullover that once belonged to her fat Uncle Bert bounces into the room. The woman is smiling cheerily.

WOMAN: Hey, kids! I've got a great idea. Why don't we have a real Saturday morning breakfast for a change? [Slowly, the children raise their eyes to gaze at her]

	Bacon, eggs, the lot! [Slowly, the children turn their eyes to one another] I'll cook!
MAN:	[Appearing in the doorway and blinking as though he thinks there's a possibility that he's entered the wrong kitchen] Huh? Did I hear someone say bacon and eggs?
CHILD 1:	[Looking and sounding suspicious] Mum just said she's going to cook breakfast.
CHILD 2:	[Looking and sounding suspicious] For us.
MAN:	[Scratching his head] That's what I thought she said.
WOMAN:	That is what I said. It's not that unusual is it?
CHILD 1:	[Exchanging significant look with child 2] What's up, Mum? You don't usually encourage us to eat large meals in front of you. Have aliens taken over your body?
CHILD 2:	Are you putting us up for adoption or something?
WOMAN:	[Laughing] Nothing's up, Chester. [Laughing more] Of course I'm not putting you up for adoption, Harmony. I just thought a cooked breakfast would be fun for a change. [Children through the ages have been smiled on as she now smiles on hers, but usually by wolves or witches.] We could have fried bread. We could even grill some tomatoes.

MAN: [Wistfully] And mushrooms?

WOMAN: [Darting around the kitchen, opening doors and drawers] And muffins! And chips!

CHILD 1: [To child 2] Muffins?

CHILD 2: [To child 1] Chips?

MAN: [Peering over woman's shoulder as she emerges from cupboard with several jars in her hands] Do we have any marmalade? Didn't we used to have some strawberry jam?

CHILD 1: [Looking shrewd] What about your diet, Mum?

CHILD 2: [Looking calculating] I thought cooked breakfasts ruined your metabolism or something.

WOMAN: [Gaily, even devil-may-carely] Don't be silly! My diet doesn't start till tomorrow!

ALL: [In sudden understanding] Oh.

SCENE TWO. Kitchen. Interior. An hour later. There are dirty frying pans on top of the cooker. There are dirty plates on the table and a few bowls with bits of food in them on the counter. The woman is alone in the kitchen. She is cleaning up. She picks up the pan the beans were heated in and scrapes the remains onto the serving spoon. She brings it to her lips.

VOICE: Woman! Is that wise?

WOMAN: What difference is another spoonful or two going to make? [She swallows beans]

VOICE: But what about the first rule of the good dieter: Never eat standing up?

WOMAN: [Chucking the empty pan into the sink and moving on to the chip bowl] I'm not on a diet.

VOICE: What about the second rule: Never nibble?

WOMAN: I'm not on a diet. [She uses the leftover chips to get up the last bits of marmalade, strawberry jam and ketchup]

VOICE: What about the third rule: Beware the hidden calorie!

WOMAN: Can't you understand English? I'm not on a diet.

VOICE: But you will be.

WOMAN: And I will be dead. [Giggles] Eat, drink and be merry, for tomorrow you diet! [She gobbles up the chips left in the serving bowl and then gobbles up the few remaining on her children's plates]

VOICE: You'll feel guilty about this tomorrow.

WOMAN: [She mops up some spilled marmalade with a cold piece of toast] No, I won't. Tomorrow's the diet. If I eat so much as one chip after tomorrow I'll feel guilty. But not today. Today's the fling. It's like when a man spends the night before his wedding in a whorehouse. Does he feel guilty? Of course not! [She helps herself to the mushrooms left stranded on her son's dish] Well, neither do I!

SCENE THREE. Front room. Interior. Same Day. Afternoon. The boy and the girl sit in front of the television, watching a film. They look up as their father enters the room. He is wearing a worried expression and holding a small address book in his hand.

CHILD 1:   Any luck?

MAN: Uncle John says she picked up Aunt Miranda at about one and they went into town for lunch.

CHILD 2:   Uh oh. What if they went to that place where you can eat all the salad, bread and dessert you want for free?

CHILD 1:   [In a surge of confidence] Don't you remember? They won't let her in there anymore. [He discreetly lowers his voice] Not after last time. [Turning to father as a new thought strikes him] Dad.... Is Aunt Miranda on a diet?

MAN: [Collapsing on sofa with a restrained groan, head in hands] She's starting tomorrow. [Children exchange a worried look]

CHILD 2:   [Sitting beside her father and putting a tiny arm around him] Don't worry, Dad. They'll be all right. After all, it's only lunch. And if they're not allowed back in Buffet Bonanza ...

MAN: [We can see that he is very upset, that his imagination is getting the better of him, but when he turns to his daughter his smile is brave] You're right, love, there's nothing to be concerned about.

They've only gone out for lunch. I'm sure your mother will be back soon. I'm sure she wouldn't do anything silly. Anything to jeopardize our happy home. [His voice is choked as he adds, in a whisper] You know how much she loves you both.

CHILD 1: [Stands on other side of father, and silently puts a small hand on his shoulder] We love her too, Dad, in spite of everything.

MAN: I know you do, love. So do I.

FADES as the three stare out towards the audience.

SCENE FOUR. Interior. Same Day. Same Time. We are in a large, popular, family restaurant. At a table between the rather gargantuan buffet areas sit two women. Though she is wearing a curly red wig and dark glasses she wasn't wearing before, we recognize one as *our* woman. The two women are eating with gusto from their overladen plates.

WOMAN: [Eating. Smiling happily. She is obviously in a good mood, and obviously enjoying herself. Her laughter is the laughter of a schoolgirl. Her appetite the appetite of a horse or a teenage boy] This is what it must have been like in the war, don't you think, Miranda?

MIRANDA: [She is also smiling, happy, and eating with enthusiastic and unconcealed enjoyment. All the time she talks she deals with her generous portions] I don't think the food could have been this good.

WOMAN: [Laughing] No, no, that's not what I meant. I meant the soldiers, you know, on their last night of leave. There they are, knowing that tomorrow they're going to be shipped to the front, that most of them will never return, or not return in one piece, and that these last few hours might be their last chance for happiness. [She pauses, gazing philosophically at her baked potato]

MIRANDA: You mean the feeling of being liberated from the usual restraints, conventions and constrictions of society by the imminence of death?

WOMAN: Exactly.

MIRANDA: Pass the mustard. Well, I for one am glad we're not at war. Can you imagine having to face your diet on ersatz chocolate and powdered eggs? My God!

WOMAN: I must say, though, Miranda, this wig was a stroke of genius. I'd never have got by that head waiter without it. [She gives a darting, sideways glance to the room, as though she expects the head-waiter to suddenly materialize] Remember when Ellie and I came here before we went on the apricot diet? He accused us of being saboteurs sent over by McDonald's. Can you imagine? You should have seen the fuss he made! He just kept shouting over and over, 'Unlimited does not mean for ever! Unlimited does not mean for ever!' Why do they say 'all you can eat' if they don't mean it?

MIRANDA: I got the idea from Mary LeMay. Remember when she was living in that village, in 1987? She and Edith Wallace had a bet about which one of them was going to go off their diet first, and Mary was doing really well, you know, 900 calories a day, fifteen laps around the churchyard, the works. And then the full moon came, and you know what Mary's like when there's a full moon. Even dieters get the blues, don't they? Anyway, she had this incredible craving for chocolate, you know how it is. She ransacked the kids' rooms but all she could find were two chocolate buttons covered in fluff and a Mars Bar wrapper with a couple of crumbs in it. In the end, she wound up standing on the kitchen sink, trying to scrape up spilled cocoa powder from the cupboard. But it was when she found herself seriously considering Tinkerbell's chocolate-flavoured cat treats that she decided it was time for something drastic. Only, of course, in a tiny village like that there wasn't a three-year-old or a budgerigar who didn't know about the bet. Edith's spies were all over the place. So she dressed up as an American tourist and just walked into the newsagent's, bold as brass, bought two family bars of fruit-and-nut and walked back out again. Simple but brilliant. [She mops up the last of the salad dressing and a few scraps of spring onion from her salad bowl with the last of her roll and looks

	up with a smile] I'll get more bread if you fill up the salad plates.
WOMAN:	What about dessert?
MIRANDA:	[Looks at her watch] It's early yet. There's still plenty of time for that. It's going to be a long while before potato salad touches these lips again.

SCENE FIVE. Bedroom. That Same Night. The room is dark. We can just about make out the bed and the fact that it is occupied.

MAN:	[Sleepily] What a day, huh, darling? I really thought for a while there that we wouldn't see you till the morning. [Laughs, but less from humour than relief] Remember that time before you and Miranda went on the peach and pasta diet, and John and I spent the entire night before trying to track you down from one fast food place to another? Where was it we finally caught up with you? Spud-U-Like or Burger King? [He moves] Or was that the time we found you in Leicester Square at one of those all-night ice cream stalls? Dear me! John was really scared that time. I can still remember pushing our way through those seedy crowds ... [his voice shudders] ... forcing our way into these tiny shops packed with tourists and John saying over and over, 'This isn't just anybody, you know, Bob, this isn't just another compulsive dieter we're talking about here, this is the

mother of my children.' Jesus. Do you know I actually had to remind him that I was going through the same thing? Can you beat that? Then he had this whole crazy theory that it must be genetic or something, because you and Miranda are sisters and your mother's been dieting for the last fifty years. 'It's not so bad for you, Bob,' he told me, 'you've only got Harmony to worry about. I've got three girls. What do you think the future looks like for me?' [He lifts himself up on one elbow] Darling, isn't that something? [More awake] Sweetheart? [Fully awake now] Christine, Baby, are you there? [The light goes on. Christine Baby is not there. A look of unadulterated terror comes over the man's face] Christine!? [He looks under the bed. We hear a fridge door slam shut off-stage. He picks up the alarm clock on the bedside table. 11.45] Oh my God!!!

SCENE SIX. Kitchen. There is a small light on near the cooker. The room is dark, but it is possible to make out a lone figure sitting at the table. There are things piled up in front of her but it is hard to distinguish them in the dim.

MAN: [Snaps on the overhead light. We can now see that the table top is littered with empty jam jars, packets and boxes, and half a banana cake with chocolate icing] Christine! What are you doing? Haven't you had enough?

WOMAN: [Doesn't so much as glance at him] I've
           got twelve more minutes, Bob. Twelve
           more minutes. Don't you understand?
           I've got to get rid of everything before
           my diet starts!

MAN: But darling, what's left? [Picking up an
           empty peanut butter jar] You've just
           about cleared out the fridge and the
           pantry as it is. [For the first time he
           takes in the fact that she is systemati-
           cally, and pretty quickly, eating her way
           through a substantial hunk of cake. His
           expression   clouds]   Christine,   love,
           where did this cake come from? There
           wasn't any cake in the house. All we had
           were those biscuits for pudding tonight.

WOMAN: Bob, please, I don't have time to discuss
           this now.

MAN: Christine, where did this cake come
           from? [A sudden look of inspiration
           comes over him. He reaches out and
           touches it] Jesus Christ! It's frozen!
           That's the cake that was in the freezer!
           It's hard as a rock!

WOMAN: [Slapping his hand out of her way] Eight
           minutes, Bob. I've only got eight
           minutes left!

7.

Choosing the Diet That's Right For You

Okay, so you've taken a good long look at yourself in several full-length mirrors; you've asked the opinions of your dearest friends and your mother (your mother, being your mother and not someone else's, usually says, 'Of course I don't think you've put on too much weight, dear,' a sure sign that you're at least as big as a bungalow; your dearest friends, being your dearest friends and not your mother, usually say, 'Well....'); you've pinched the inch and found a yard; and the love of your life, wrapping his arms around you in the night, has whispered into your ear, 'Pandora, sweetie, are you the only other person in this bed, or is there a sumo wrestler in here, too?' You decide to go on a diet.

The question now is: which diet? For although it is true that, having seen one spitting cobra you have pretty much seen all spitting cobras, it is not true that a diet by any other name is still 1,200 calories and a sensible programme of exercise. Every diet, as every lifetime dieter knows (or soon finds out), is different. Every diet has its own set of advantages and disadvantages, built-in pitfalls and hidden strengths. Like each dieter, each diet has a unique personality; a nature peculiar only to itself. And though over the years, of course, you will probably try every diet ever created at least once, a lot of time, money and anguish can be saved if you know from the start that you will last exactly two-and-a-half hours on the kumquat and trampoline diet, but actually lose five pounds and not try to murder your children on the low carbohydrate and aerobics one.

Counting Versus Crashing

Jane says that when she was first starting out on her career as a serious dieter, there were two fundamental kinds of diets. The first was your basic control diet where you counted something. Usually this something was calories, but sometimes it was carbohydrates or fats, and sometimes it was a combination of things. The second was your basic quick-weight-loss crash diet, into which category fell most single-food fad diets (e.g., all the avocados you could eat and a glass of water). The counting diet was meant to be scientific and sensible, to establish a pattern of eating that would hold down your weight once the diet was over, and not to kill you or ruin your sense of humour once and for all. The crashing diet was meant to get rid of those pounds, and get rid of them pretty damn quick, even if it meant putting every cell in your body into a state of trauma from which they would never recover.

'Oh, hang on, Serena,' says Jane. 'Some of the so-called fad diets I've been on that you disparage so much have been excellent. Truly truly excellent.'

Like that liquid one you gained fifteen pounds on in 1988?

'I didn't gain fifteen pounds on the diet, Serena, and you know it. It was when I went back to solids that I lost all control.'

Like the scratch-and-sniff diet? Jane paid a small fortune for a book of photographs of food. It had everything — exotic banquets, substantial soups, ethnic snacks, Black Forest gateau with vanilla ice cream and hot fudge sauce — enough of a range to gratify every dieter's taste. You were supposed to choose your food, staring lovingly down at the excellent reproduction of detail and colour, and then you were supposed to scratch the panel at the side, and the fragrant aroma of the apple pie or the linguine and clam sauce you were drooling over would gently waft through the room. You were not supposed to be so driven by hunger and the effectiveness of the sniff pad that you ate the picture.

'These things happen,' says Jane.

How about that sponsored slim you went on, Jane? The one where you ended up paying your sponsors?

'Oh, for Pete's sake, Serena. It wasn't the organizers' fault that their slim started on the day Daniel Foxman left me for a *Vogue* model, was it? I'm sure it would've worked otherwise.'

So, okay, Jane, what have been your truly excellent fad diets?

'Well, how about the ice cream diet?' says Jane. 'I went from a size ten to a size nine in eight days on the ice cream diet. You always forget that, don't you?'

What I remember, Jane, is that last summer when we went to Italy, a country that has raised the making of ice cream to a major art form, you turned green every time we passed a gelateria.

'The raisin and sour cream diet. A pound a day for two weeks.'

Protein deficiency and a touch of anaemia.

'Chocolate and white rice, Serena? I lasted six weeks on chocolate and white rice and was able to wear those satin hot pants that once belonged to Cher for seven.'

Beri-beri.

'Okay, Serena, okay. What about the grape diet? Huh? What about that? You went on it at the same time I did, if I remember correctly. And you were raving about it at the time.'

It's true. For three glorious days I gobbled up grapes with gay abandon. Every time I demurely weighed myself, the scales, instead of crying out in horror and alarm, 'Oh, my God! What have you been eating now?', sighed happily and dropped down another four or five ounces. But then I began waking in the middle of the night, feverish with desire for things other than grapes: goat's cheese; macaroni with tomato sauce; sweet and sour pork; yams baked with peanuts. At work, I'd sit at my desk, my eyes on the terminal and my mind on spinach soufflé. Out for a night on the town with Paul Newman, all I could talk about was his recipe for salad dressing. After a week and a half of this I went to an Indonesian restaurant and consumed four servings of gado gado as only a boa constrictor or a woman who has been eating nothing but grapes for nearly two weeks could consume them. After that, I didn't touch wine for a year and a half. To this day, passing a fruit store causes that little voice who is the shop steward of my body to call out, 'Please, we'll do whatever you want, but no more grapes!'

'Okay, Serena, okay,' concedes Jane. 'I do admit that one of the drawbacks to the crash diet is malnutrition and that another is its temporary nature. But then you have to admit that the counting diet isn't much better.'

I admit it. You wind up measuring biscuits and wondering if a square cracker is less fattening than a round one. You come to believe that if you eat one teaspoon of sweet pickle a day over your body's required calorie intake, you will put on thirty pounds in the next ten years (or fifteen in five; six in two; three in one; a pound and a half in six short months).

Can you grasp the significance of that? A pound and a half in six months, all because you eat one teaspoon of sweet pickle too much a day. That's a pretty scary thought. It's like being in one of those fairy tales where (although you don't know it, and although even if you did know, it wouldn't be of any protection to you) if you prick your finger on a thorn at five o'clock on your seventeenth birthday you're going to sleep for a hundred years or turn into a marine iguana. If one teaspoon of sweet pickle will do that, what happens if you inadvertently eat one chocolate digestive extra in the course of a day? What happens if the sandwich you buy for lunch every day isn't 375 calories, as you have determined through a rigorous grading system, but 475 because the cheese it is made with comes from fat cows and the bread has wheatgerm added and is made with milk, not water? What happens if your mother has been lying to you all these years and she doesn't really make her mashed potatoes with skimmed milk and low-fat margarine, but real butter and real milk? Abracadabra! One day you look quite normal and the next you're a dead ringer for a prehistoric monster with a fondness for algae. Why, may the saints preserve us, this means that if you were in a situation where you were breathing in peanut sauce or white lasagne fumes every day you could put on an extra three pounds a month. Three pounds a month for the rest of your life! Just by breathing!

'So what does this mean?' you rightly want to know. 'That there's no use in dieting? That no diet works?'

As you would expect, opinions do differ.

But Jane says, 'No!' A bold, strong, resonant and emphatic 'No!' Jane says that, in fact, all diets work, to some extent, and at least for a while. But that there are special diets (most of them invented by her) that work better, or that used in conjunction with a more conventional diet (mango and pineapple, for example) will not only make it cover all sorts of extenuating circumstances and emergency situations, but will actually transform the diet from a short-term regimen to a permanent part of your life.

The Restaurant Diet

Jane invented the restaurant diet in 1982.

'The what?' you ask.

The restaurant diet. It was at a time when she was having a lot of business lunches and even dinners. 'You know what it's like,' says Jane. 'In order to get ahead in your career, you have to go to all these boring expensive restaurants and sit through three-course meals with men who wear platinum watches and carry portable phones. Well, needless to say, you're not going to make a big impression if you refuse a menu and inform the waiter that you're only eating oranges this week, are you?'

And Jane, of course, is right. For many professional women, it is the business lunch that makes it impossible for her to win the battle with her hips, no matter how great her will power or how good her diet. But for any dieter, whether she eats out once a day as a matter of course, or once a month as a treat after a film, the simple act of walking into a restaurant can cast all resolve back out on the street. Think of it.

You step out of the world of measured portions and into a world where it is difficult to estimate the calorie content of the broccoli mousse or the double bacon-and-blue-cheese burger with barbecued onions. You pick up the menu and discover that the asparagus is young and fresh and accompanied by a hollandaise sauce like a hymn. 'What the hell,' you tell yourself, 'I'll diet tomorrow.' You look up at the board and discover that the chips are jumbo and that the Texas medley made Clint Eastwood cry. 'I won't eat for the next two days,' you say. Tender lamb, delicately sautéed carrots, chilli-cheese nachos, Cajun black fish ... putting a dieter in a restaurant is like putting Warren Beatty in a girls' school and expecting him to stay in his room. So difficult is it to maintain your diet equilibrium in such a situation that most dieters who have to face the business lunch on a regular basis just throw their hands in the air and resign themselves to never wearing lycra dresses.

'It was hell,' says Jane. 'It was simply hell. Dante couldn't have come up with anything more fiendish or tortuous. If you ordered the grilled fish without potatoes, just a green salad, no dressing, the person you were dining with would almost always smirk in that way people who aren't on a diet smirk, and then he'd say, "Don't tell me *you're* on a diet, hahaha." Well, naturally, you didn't want to tell this perfect stranger who held your entire promising career in his hands that you'd been on a diet since you were twelve, did you? You didn't want to admit publicly that the reason you didn't look like a tug boat was that you lived on carrots and water and made yourself vomit whenever you ate chocolate custard with cream. On the other hand, however, you didn't want to actually eat, either. For a while I thought maybe it would work if I skipped breakfast, ate lunch, skipped supper, and didn't eat at the weekend. But that turned out to be a disaster, because at about ten at night I'd start to feel hungry and I'd think, well, there must've been about five hundred calories just in the sauce that was on the cauliflower at lunch. I might as well have some cottage cheese and a couple of sticks of celery. And the next thing you'd know I'd be eating breakfast and stuffing my face at the weekend — it just shot my discipline to hell.'

But then, fortuitously, Jane hit upon the restaurant diet. Simple, effective and virtually foolproof, it was, to say the least, a stroke of genius. With the restaurant diet Jane could luncheon anywhere she wanted, starter and dessert included, and never gain an ounce.

'Not an ounce?'

Not one. In fact, the pounds melted away like butter on a hot potato.

'What's the catch?'

There is no catch. That, says Jane, is the beauty of the restaurant diet. You don't even have to take up jogging or abseiling. All you have to do is order things you don't like.

'Excuse me?'

You order things you don't like — or, preferably, hate and find loathsome. Things you wouldn't eat on a bet. Things you would eat on a bet, but it'd have to be a pretty big bet — say over two hundred thousand. If you love beef, but hate it rare, order it rare. If you love chocolate cake but hate it with cream, order it with cream. Thousand island dressing makes you retch? Have them drown your salad in it. Have them pour some over your main course. Does shellfish make you nauseous? Does pork make your hair fall out? Then order away! Simple? Yes. Foolproof. Just about.

Jane and I went out to celebrate this diet shortly after its conception.

'I don't know why I never thought of this before,' said Jane happily, moving the mussels around her plate, turning up her nose at the rabbit braised in tomato sauce and biting into a crust of dry bread, smiling with joy on the parslied potatoes, passing me her Russian salad.

'Me neither,' I said glumly. For if there was one catch to the restaurant diet it was my mother. My mother raised me to hate waste, especially when you're paying for it. So what happened was that after I'd finished my meal I finished Jane's. She lost five pounds that night and I gained ten.

The Holiday Diet

Jane came up with the holiday diet when I was trying to convince her to go to Madrid with me one summer. I'd been trying for six years to get her to agree to go away with me. 'Oh, no,' she kept saying, 'I know what happens to people who go away on holiday.'

They get tanned? They have a good time? They fall in love with the waiter in the local chuleta house?

'They gain weight.'

Oh come on, Jane, I argued, everybody who goes on holiday does not gain weight.

'No,' said Jane, 'there is some truth in that. People who go to Moscow don't gain weight until they get back. In most cases, however, going on holiday is like going into a war zone. You lose touch with reality. You're not sure you'll ever return. If you do return you will be totally changed. Away from the familiar structures and restraints of your own, stable, society, your normal patterns of behaviour break down. You forget that you never eat lunch. You who usually have one dry slice of toast with a cup of black coffee every morning start putting butter and jam on your three hunks of toasted bread. Black coffee becomes a thing of the past. You grow more and more careless.

"What the hell," you say, "I'm on holiday!" There's nothing else to do so you not only eat three meals a day, you stop every hour or two for a snack. You drink from noon on. You have to try all the local delicacies, even the things you....'

So all right, I said, we'll go to Scotland. The local delicacies there are all things like haggis, tablet and pressed oats, things nobody in her right mind would eat.

'Scotland?' said Jane. 'Have you gone mad? In Scotland they serve chips with everything, even spaghetti. Even cheese salad. Even pudding. Black Forest gateau and chips.' She shuddered. 'We might as well be locked in a kitchen with my mother for a month.'

Well, surely, I said, the solution is simply to employ the restaurant diet. But extend it to three meals a day. What could be easier? It's exactly the same thing, after all.

'But it's not the same thing at all,' said Jane. 'The idea behind the restaurant diet is that it supplements your normal diet. That's how it works, by making sure you don't go off the diet you're actually on. But if you're living in some hut on a Greek beach, where the dieter's staples like grapefruit and cottage cheese and All Bran are a little thin on the ground, or in some quaint hotel by the North Sea, where fresh vegetables are viewed with suspicion, you've got a little problem, haven't you? You can't hope to maintain your normal regimen. Are you with me, Serena?'

Um.

'Look, it's really simple. Back home, you can order crab mayonnaise for lunch, because you know that crab makes your skin break out so you wouldn't touch it with a barbecue fork. But the other reason you order it is because you know that when you get home you'll be able to eat all the grapefruit you want, or you've still got 635 calories to squander on a lean hamburger and a leaf of lettuce. If you thought the crab was all you were going to get, though, you'd eventually succumb, even at the risk of turning your forehead into a beacon and your hips into boulders.' She rolled her eyes. 'And Spain! My God, Serena, I really think you're losing it. They dip bread in *olive oil* in Spain. They just dip it right in, like it's yoghurt or something. They don't think anything's cooked unless it's fried. And they drink *red* wine.'

Yes, well, I said, I see what you mean. The Spanish do have a thing about olive oil, and it's true that crispbread hasn't yet made a really big impact on their consciousness, but I still couldn't help feeling that there must be some way to make holidaying compatible with dieting. We just weren't looking at this from the right angle. Obviously, one of those package deals was out because the food was all paid for, and Germany had all that beer and those rich desserts, and Italy had all that pasta, and Israel had all those Jewish mothers, and....

And then Jane got it.

'I've got it!' she cried. 'The holiday diet! My God, I think they should give me a special Nobel Prize.'

The idea is to go somewhere where there is no chance that food is going to prove a temptation. Mountain climbing in the Himalayas. Camping in the Arctic. Sighseeing in Beirut.

We went to Thailand. She wanted to go to Burma, because of the hostilities (which, Jane reasoned, were guaranteed to keep food supplies down and metabolism levels up), and there was even some mention of Cambodia, and India, of course, was a top contender ('Oh, amoebic dysentery, pooh,' said Jane. 'What price a size eight, that's what I always say.'), but in the end she settled for Thailand. Because of the lizards, as much as anything. 'You can't really overeat if you're constantly worried about something green and pink with buggy little eyes falling into your food, can you?' asked Jane. A point worth making.

The Difficult Venue Diet

A slightly more sophisticated and long-term version of the holiday diet, the difficult venue diet works on the same basic principle. You deliberately put yourself in a place or situation where it is hard enough to maintain your weight, never mind gain any.

Third World countries, especially those in the grips of civil war, famine, or (as often happens) both, come highly recommended, and it is, of course, advisable, if your sojourn is for less than a year, to select a time when the roads will be washed out by heavy rains and the incidence of the more debilitating diseases is at its highest.

Prisons and hospitals are also possible options (though it goes without saying that you do not want to be in either for anything serious enough to make the question of your diet a rather moot point). In both cases, the food is bad, you never get enough of it, and you can't nip down to the local Indian for a stuffed paratha whenever you feel that life's not up to par. As long as you don't have well-intentioned visitors bringing you boxes of candied fruit and chocolates every week, a few months in either of these institutions should help you shed those pounds relatively effortlessly. Jane does point out, however, that the boredom of confinement can sometimes present a problem. Even bad food can seem like a good thing if the high point of your day is walking down to the nurse's station or taking a turn around the exercise yard. And also remember that institutional cuisine traditionally makes up in stodge what it lacks in nutritional value. So Jane advises that you plan in advance. Choose a jail or hospital that is relatively modern and up-to-date, one that has recreational facilities and activities, and one that at least occasionally gives you the option of spinach salad over mashed potatoes.

Aeroplanes (though not, it must be quickly pointed out, airports, where there is easy access to concentrated calories in the form of sweets, pastry and the larded bread graced by a leaf of dead lettuce that they call sandwiches) and long-distance buses are other good locations for the dedicated dieter. There is never anything to eat on a plane, aside, perhaps, from a roll or a couple of crackers and, if you're really lucky, an apple. And if there is something to eat, you know you'll never get more than one serving, and that that one serving wouldn't be enough to stuff a hamster. Buses are even better, because they don't serve food at all (although they do stop at motorway service stations, very close sisters of the airport, and just as dangerous). In both instances, if you get a sudden urge to fill your cheeks with chocolate éclairs in the middle of the journey there is nowhere to go to get a snack.

'Just imagine a job where you travel three months out of every four, where you spend most of the time in the air or getting to the airport or coming back from the airport,' says Jane. 'A job where as soon as you've finished with one appointment or meeting, it's time to get on a jumbo and go to another. If you had a job like that you'd be a seven-and-a-half in no time.'

Well, that is true Jane. Either that or dead. And it does sound pretty good — working, seeing the world and losing weight all at the same time — but exactly what sort of job would that be? Gunrunning? Drugs smuggling? Fundraiser for some terrorist group?

'Rock star,' says Jane with her usual clarity and directness of thought. 'Rock stars are always in planes or buses. They spend years and years on the road, just going from one hotel to the next. They always arrive at three in the morning, when the kitchen's closed. They're too nervous before the show to eat and too tired afterward. And, even better, they work off about three million calories a performance. Look at how skinny they all are! Bob Dylan. Richie Sambora. Alice Cooper. Mick Jagger. Steve Tyler. Prince. Nils Lofgren's probably never bought anything in the men's department in his life.'

But, Jane, all the rock stars you've mentioned are men.

'Well most real rock stars are, Serena. I mean, with a few notable exceptions like Cher and Tina Turner, women in rock tend to be chubby and sing background.'

But if rock is one of those occupations, like racing and mercenary soldiering, that discourages much serious female participation, doesn't that limit this a little?

'No diet's perfect, Serena, you said so yourself.'

The Mega-Stress Diet

It is, says Jane, a well-documented fact that certain kinds of stress work on your appetite as the atomic bomb works on highly populated areas. Other kinds have such an effect on your metabolism that you burn up calories almost as soon as they hit your tongue. So what the dieter needs is to put herself in situations where stress (instead of just making her hair fall out, her skin go spotty, or her sense of humour shrivel to the size of a pea) is working for her, helping make her diet an unqualified success.

Well, um, Jane, when you say 'mega-stress', what exactly do you mean? You're not suggesting that we all book cabins on the *Titanic* are you? You're not suggesting a trip to Iran?

'No, of course not, Serena. What do you think I am? I mean, I suppose if you look at it one way, death is the ultimate diet, but all things have their time and place, don't they? I'm not saying that you actually put your life in jeopardy or anything. though I still think Burma wasn't such a bad idea.'

So what are you suggesting?

'There are easily accessible, everyday events and situations that produce a great deal of stress and anxiety with a minimal amount of effort.'

Like what?

'Like an adulterous affair.'

You what?

'Nothing burns up the calories as quickly as a romantic liaison in which one or both of the participants is married to someone else,' says Jane.

I can't believe I'm hearing this. You're advocating infidelity?

'Within reason, Serena, and for the sake of your hips.'

Jane!

'Oh, for Pete's sake Serena, don't get your chest expander in a twist. I'm not actually promoting the extramarital affair. I'm just saying that if you're having one, you might as well get something out of it besides all those broken promises and nights you sit by yourself crying because he hasn't rung.' Jane winks. 'I call it angst exercise. It's easier and less dangerous than aerobics and you can wear anything you want.'

Well, I suppose that Jane, as usual, is not without her point. Next to heavy duty exercise, nothing gobbles up those calories like stress; and what is an illicit affair but stress with a few hasty kisses and runny mascara? Let's imagine that you, a happily married dieter, are having an affair with a man you met on the train one morning. Let's further imagine a day in your life....

You and your lover meet after a separation of two weeks. This meeting, difficult to arrange (it was all set, then his son came down with the mumps; it was all set, then your husband's football game was cancelled; it was all set, but that night he was stuck in a lift for four hours; it was all set, but you crashed the car on the way to the hotel) (— 4,568 calories) and short in duration, takes place in the flat of a friend. Though you arrive late (— 651 calories), you arrive first. You have to circle the block several times because you thought you saw a very good friend of your husband's coming out of a house down the street (— 5,000 calories). You finally park the car in the dark alley and then, hunched over with your collar up and your hat over your eyes, you sprint to the rendezvous. You accidentally ring the bell for the flat upstairs and drop the keys in what might be mud. You're shaking by the time you reach the living room (— 939 calories). You sit on the sofa. You peer, very carefully, out of the window. You stand up. You walk into the kitchen. You come back. You look out of the window. An hour unpleasantly passes in this way (— 1,977 calories). Eventually your love, who found your directions confusing and has been driving on, over, and off the flyover for the past forty-five minutes, looking for the 'left at the plumbing supply store' you mentioned in your instructions, arrives. By now you are not only feeling fairly slender, by now you and he have exactly fifty-seven minutes left, including the time allotted for hello, goodbye, how are you, and oh, I've missed you so much. You use up sixty-eight minutes (— 682 calories), and then there is an incredible scrabble to get dressed and out of the flat before its owner returns home and your husband sends the police out after you (— 1,751 calories). When you get home, late (— 899 calories), and without the milk and mince you were supposed to pick up on the way (— 290 calories), you realize that the silver locket your husband gave you for your birthday is no longer around your neck (at this discovery, the equivalent of three chocolate bars and a bacon sandwich is immediately zapped by your body). While your husband is trying to come to grips with your daughter's maths homework, you turn both kitchen taps on full force and start banging pots and pans around, and use up the calorie value of a Big Mac and fries while you phone the friend who loaned you the flat. She isn't there (life now owes you a chocolate milkshake as well). You dial the number of your paramour (— 7,894.5 calories). His wife answers (you now understand why all the femme fatales of fact and fiction always seem to be so thin). If, before you wordlessly hang up on his wife, your husband gets on the extension with a, 'Darling, who's that you're talking to?', your body will consume half of its own weight in approximately 2.3 seconds. Every time the telephone rings that night you jump three feet in the air and incinerate 250 calories. You console yourself with the thought of how much weight you'd lose if you and your demon lover, passionately snogging in an alleyway thirty miles from home, were suddenly to look up and see Mrs Demon Lover looking in. You'd probably never have to go on another diet till the end of the next millennium.

But surely, Jane, there are other calorie-disintegrating situations that don't involve homewrecking or possible homicide.

'Naturally,' says Jane.

Besides 'naturally', Jane says that shopping in superstores is a good way of consuming energy.

But I thought that food shopping was something the committed dieter should never do. Not unless she's just eaten a three-course meal and a goodly snack. Not unless she's blindfolded and has a clothespeg over her nose. Not unless she's with someone who is going to check every item placed in the basket and say, 'Out. Get it out. There's no way garlic dressing and smoked almonds are on your diet.'

'Old wive's tale,' says Jane. 'There's nothing like four or five hours in Sainsbury's to jangle those nerves and burn off that sludge. Even if you haven't eaten in three days and have been filling the cart like the food's all free, you'll still lose weight.'

You do, though, have to choose your time and circumstances carefully. There's no point in going at two o'clock on a Wednesday when the aisles are clear and you don't have to strain to hear the musak over the shouts and wails of small, demented children. There's no point going on a night when you're bored and lonely and wouldn't mind standing in a queue for an hour or two while the couple in front of you lays out the grounds for their impending divorce.

Jane says that the best times are Friday nights, Saturday mornings, or three o'clock on a Thursday afternoon. These are the times when everyone, her brother, her husband, and her thirteen screaming brats will be jamming the aisles and causing queues reminiscent of Dusseldorf during the war. She further says that the best state to be in is a hurry. The bigger the hurry and the more crowded the store, the greater the rate at which you'll burn off calories. For instance, if you're trying to get home in time to watch *Cheers* and the man in front of you in the deli queue holds everything up for eleven minutes while he rings his wife on his portable phone to find out if she said cheddar or cheshire, you probably won't lose more than an ounce or two. But let's say you're in a hurry because your boss (the gourmet) and Mel Gibson (the actor) are coming to dinner. The store couldn't be more crowded if they were giving the stuff away. No one except you has come with less than three children, and not one of these children is in a quiet, pensive mood. Nor, oddly enough, have any of these children been told that it is bad manners to open packets of crisps, throw fruit or small sweets at each other, hurl themselves on the floor with anguished screams when their mothers won't let them have a frozen fish finger, or puke up on other shoppers. Is it any wonder, then, that it takes you fifteen minutes just to negotiate the four yards between the lettuces and the onions, and (trapped on the soup aisle by six small children playing bumper cars with their mothers' carts) another three-quarters of an hour to battle your way from dairy products to baked goods? You're finally ready to pay for your groceries and race home to whip up the borscht and the beef stroganoff. You look at the queue. You rub your eyes. You look at your watch. The queue at the checkout is four-and-a-half miles long. You look at your watch. But what are your options? If you abandon your cart and go elsewhere, will your boss and Mel have to wait on the doorstep less time than they will if you get behind the family of giants with the three trolleys? Will they have to stand there longer? Or will the amount of time they pace back and forth in front of your building in the pouring rain be exactly the same? Better the devil you know than the devil you don't, as your mother always said. By the time you are being checked out and the cashier has run the whipped cream over the bar code reader fifteen times before she admits defeat and rings it in manually, you have burned up 300,000 calories and have to hold your skirt up as you run to the car.

'Pretty good, huh?' gloats Jane. 'Sometimes I go shopping on a Saturday morning whether I need to or not. And there are lots more similar activities, believe you me. Anybody who gets all sweaty jogging when she could just be doing angst exercising is out of her mind.'

What follows is the Jane Forbes-Smythe Guide to Mega-Stress Exercise (or What You Can Eat Without Ruining Your Diet If You Are in This Situation Chart):

Situation
Trying to find a parking space in any major city (especially London, Washington D.C. and Rome, and especially when you've paid what in 1937 would have been a deposit on a house in Slough for the theatre tickets) and most large shopping centres (or outside your own home when you have with you three tons of groceries, a crying toddler and an Alsatian who refuses to walk).

Food Equivalent Devoured under Pressure (FEDUP)
Three packets of salt and vinegar crisps.

Situation
Waiting for the repairman ('He'll be right there').

FEDUP
Two fairy cakes and a glass of milk.

Situation
Waiting for the repairman ('He's on his way') while your living-room furniture floats down the hallway.

FEDUP
Three whisky sours, one packet of mini Swiss rolls and a bowl of shrimp dip.

Situation
Getting a flat tyre in the desert just as twilight descends.

FEDUP
Two double-avocado burgers, onion rings and an apple pie.

Situation
Getting a flat tyre in the desert just as twilight descends and then discovering that you left the jack at home.

FEDUP
Half an ox.

Situation
Walking down empty, echoing streets by yourself very late on a dark, moonless night in any large city, especially if you're wearing high heels (goodish for a weapon, but about as much use for running as skis).

FEDUP
Half a pineapple upside-down cake.

Situation
Walking down empty, echoing streets by yourself very late on a dark, moonless night in any large city, wearing high heels, and unable to find the street you're looking for.

FEDUP
Half a pineapple upside-down cake, and a family-size tub of chocolate chip ice cream.

Situation
The streets are still empty and echoing, the night is still dark and moonless, and the city is still large and as quiet as a psychopath's smile. You know the street you want is around here somewhere — but where? And then a man materializes in a doorway. 'What's a sweetheart like you doing out on her own at this hour of night in a neighbourhood like this?' he asks. You do not speak to strangers, especially not ones who look like they ride Triumphs and have skulls tattooed on their necks, so you keep walking. It may be that you are no longer walking alone.

FEDUP
This one's worth a good 1,000,000 calories in anybody's book. The only drawback is that by the time you discover that this guy's an undercover cop, has a heart of gold and was only following you to make sure you were safe, or wasn't following you, you are in such a state that when you get home you consume 1,000,020 calories before you've even got your coat off.

Situation
You met the most incredibly wonderful man at a party last night. Handsome, intelligent, charming, funny — and what a smile, he'd put a Klieg light to shame. He walks you home and says he'll 'call you tomorrow'. Now it's tomorrow. You cancelled your plans for the evening and sit by the phone. You're afraid to go to the bathroom, let alone take your nightly shower, in case you miss his call. The news

comes and the news goes. The early chat shows come and the early chat shows go. So do the feature film, the situation comedies, the documentary on the narrow-jawed crocodile. He's not going to ring. But maybe he will. Maybe his phone's been broken all evening and he's been waiting for it to be fixed; maybe he stopped at a fast-food place for a cup of coffee on his way home from work and there was a robbery and he was held at gunpoint until eleven, and then had to go down to the police station to make a statement; maybe he had to work late and he'd left your number at home; maybe the robbers stole your number and he's been trying to get hold of your hosts to get it from them but they just left for Bolivia; maybe there's something wrong with your line; maybe you were too cool when you said goodbye and he thinks you don't want him to call; maybe he had to go to Bolivia, suddenly, and there was no time to let you know; maybe he called earlier but he got the answering machine and he doesn't speak to answering machines; maybe he does speak to answering machines but yours confused him; maybe your answering machine isn't working right; maybe he was rushing to get home to ring you and he was hit by a bus and is at this moment lying in a hospital bed, begging the nurse to bring him a phone; maybe.... At one o'clock, unlikely as it seems that he might still call, you curl up on the couch with the telephone beside you. You have bad dreams.

FEDUP
Every time the telephone rings, you burn up a sausage sandwich.

Every time the telephone doesn't ring, you burn up a sausage sandwich and a portion of chips.

You lose a pound and a half in your sleep.

Situation
Waiting for a bus.

FEDUP
One slice of toast, with jam and butter.

Situation
Waiting for a bus at night.

FEDUP
One jam doughnut and a can of cola.

Situation
Waiting for a bus on a Monday morning when you're already running late, it's pissing down, and you've got an important meeting in twenty minutes.

FEDUP
Two chocolate-glazed doughnuts and a cappuccino.

Situation
Waiting for a bus on a Saturday afternoon with two small, grumpy children, several carrier bags of shopping, a pushchair, a stuffed dinosaur and a laser gun, it's snowing, and at least one of the small, grumpy children has to go to the toilet (the other one is thirsty).

FEDUP
Two bowls of minestrone, half a loaf of garlic bread and twenty-six burnt almonds.

Situation
Travelling anywhere, in any form of transport, during rush hour.

FEDUP
A dry martini and a bag of peanuts.

Situation
You have been travelling for twelve hours in a blizzard. You finally reach your destination to discover that the hotel has given your room to someone else. Your room was the last room they had, because of the convention. And, because of the convention, there are no other rooms available in the entire city and its outlying areas.

FEDUP
A steak sandwich (with Swiss cheese and mayonnaise) and two bottles of beer (large).

Situation
You go into the local branch of a major chain store that specializes in audio-visual goods, hoping to buy a portable cassette player. You stand by the display of portable cassette players, looking interested, reading the little tags, gazing up hopefully whenever a sales assistant passes in your vicinity. You start tapping your foot and clearing your throat. You spot a sales assistant at the back of the store who is inadvertently looking in your direction, and you wave. Sales assistant waves back. Eventually a sales assistant does approach you, looking mildly curious. 'Did you want something?' sales assistant asks. You say, yes, you wanted a portable cassette player. This announcement takes the sales assistant by surprise. The sales assistant thought you'd just come in to get out of the rain, or, perhaps, because you like reading information tags. 'Maybe you'd like to show me a portable cassette player or two,' you suggest. 'Pardon?' says the sales assistant. When you finally coerce the sales assistant into showing you the machine you want, it turns out that they don't have any in stock. 'Well, couldn't you order it for me?' you

persist. This idea strikes the sales assistant as even more novel than the idea that you wanted to buy something in the first place. 'Order it?' the sales assistant queries.

FEDUP
A large portion of barbecued chicken, potato salad and hot rolls included.

Situation
Straightening out the mess the telephone company has made of your phone bill by charging you for thirteen calls to Yugoslavia that you never made.

FEDUP
Two packets of Garibaldis and a strawberry yoghurt.

Situation
Spending three days trying to straighten out the mess the telephone company has made of your phone bill but not succeeding — not even coming close.

FEDUP
A crate of Garibaldis and three chocolate milkshakes.

Situation
Waiting in a bank queue during your lunch hour.

FEDUP
A cheese sandwich, with pickle.

Situation
Waiting in a bank queue during your lunch hour on a Friday.

FEDUP
A cheese sandwich, with ham, mayonnaise, chicken and butter.

Situation
You leave Mary's birthday party, held in a trendy restaurant in the centre of town, at approximately 1.35 a.m. Just down the road is the busiest street in one of the busiest capital cities in the universe. You will get a night bus home. You reach the busiest of streets, but though there are herds of people huddled together at every bus stop, there are no buses. Tell a lie. Every thirty minutes a bus does come along, but it is never the bus you want and it is always over-full and not letting on any more passengers, the driver's very sorry, and he's sure there's a bus right behind him. You will take a taxi. It's a Saturday night in the sophisticated heart of this teeming metropolis, so, of course, there are no taxis. You will call a mini-cab. The first three call boxes you come to are broken. The fourth doesn't take money. The fifth takes money but there is someone in it, trying to convince his girlfriend not to leave him.

FEDUP
Two onion bhajis, a veggie samosa, nan bread and curried gravy.

The Broken Heart Diet

As on economic policy and the role of education in contemporary society, opinions do tend to differ on the effect love has on body weight (see Chapter Nine, Great Dieting Myths). Jane used to be of the school of thought that maintains that unhappiness puts on pounds. But after the Daniel Foxman debacle, when she sought comfort from his treachery in the depths of the crisp bag, she invented The Broken Heart Diet. Now she is of the school that believes that unrequited passion, or passion that was once requited and is no longer, can lead to a loss of appetite as well as an accompanying level of stress that sucks up those calories like there's no tomorrow (which as far as you're concerned, of course, there needn't be). Or, to put it more succinctly, a broken heart should only be good news for your thighs.

Yeah, but Jane, I say, a person can't exactly go out and get a broken heart the way she can go out and get a rowing machine or a packet of slimming pills. Can she?

And Jane agrees. She says that despite the fact that it sometimes seems that broken hearts are two a penny, you still can't actually get one on demand. 'But broken hearts are like buses,' Jane maintains. 'If you wait long enough one's bound to come your way.'

And is that something to look forward to? Is that the thought for today?

'No,' says Jane, 'the thought for today is that when one does come along you should embrace it as a friend. You should not think: here we go, I'm going to squeeze myself into the microwave and end it all. You should think: praise the Lord! I'm about to lose weight.'

But Jane....

'I know what you're going to say, Serena.'

Well, that's a relief.

'You're going to say that the first thing someone does when she finds out that Harry really isn't interested in women, or that Lionel's been sleeping with her sister for the past six months is stuff her face. Just like I did when Daniel left me.'

Amazingly enough (recalling, perhaps, not just Daniel Judas Foxman but the sixteen pounds I myself put on when Boris Zakinsky left me to find himself in Tibet and found an Australian dentist whom he married two months later instead), I was going to say something just like that.

'That's because we didn't know how to handle your broken hearts,' says Jane. 'When Boris took your backpack and went off like that, you were wallowing, not utilizing. You were thinking, "Poor me", not "What a break". You were thinking, "I'll show that bastard, I'll eat two Madeira cakes and a box of chocolates for dessert every night for three weeks. He'll be sorry." Not "Okay, Boris Zakinsky, I'm going to lose two stone, become incredibly skinny and beautiful, and have an affair with Tom Cruise that'll knock the socks off two continents. Let's just see what you think about that."'

I guess I'm just a fool for love.

'Um....' says Jane. 'Or just a fool.'

Oh, come on, Jane. Surely that's a little harsh. When a person is in the throes of anguish — when she can't see the tape measure or read the calorie chart because her eyes are filled with tears, when she can't hear the voice of her scales saying, 'Uh oh, dearie, you are now entering the twilight zone,' because the room is filled with the sound of her sobs — you can't expect her to think rationally.

'There's a right way and a wrong way to do everything,' says Jane. 'Even have a broken heart.'

The Right Way to Have a Broken Heart

1. Listen to a lot of country music. [If you don't have any Serena, then you should go out and get some. It should be as much a part of your life as your foundation and your strip wax.] Songs like 'Hello Walls', 'Tonight the Bottle Let Me Down', 'Today I Started Loving You Again', 'Am I Fool Number One?', 'I Can't Stop Loving You', 'I'm So

Lonesome I Could Cry', and 'Love Hurts' are a great way of keeping your stress level up and your appetite down. Who can hear Willie Nelson singing about a love gone wrong and think of eating? No one, that's who. You're on the floor, weeping your heart out. If you lie on the floor weeping your heart out better if you've had a few drinks than if you've had a bottle of mineral water, stick to white wine.

2. Talk about it all the time. If your friends start exhibiting signs of compassion fatigue after the first month or so (if for instance, the minute they see you they say, 'Pandora, not one more word about Freddy and the tree surgeon, or I'll slug you'), then start telling strangers. Everyone loves a good broken heart story, especially if it's not theirs. Tell the woman at the checkout in the supermarket. Tell the butcher. Let the attendant in the petrol station in on the news. Ride a lot of trains and buses. Tell the people who sit next to you what the creep did to you, how badly he hurt you, how you'll never love anyone else. Tell the ticket collector and the conductor and the woman you help up the escalator with her push-chair and her heavy shopping. For the more you talk about it, the more vivid and painful it will remain. The more vivid and painful it remains, the more weight you'll lose.

3. Practice pining. In order to practice pining you must keep pictures of the Betrayer of Your Love in strategic locations around the house. By your bed, so that you can cry yourself to sleep (there's a good five or six hundred calories gone up in smoke right there). Taped to the door of

the fridge, so that every time you go to get something to eat your throat tightens with hurt and anger and your stomach clenches. Taped to the bathroom mirror so that as you put your make-up on in the morning (brilliantly, of course, so as to hide every trace of last night's tears) you can remind yourself that the only way to make him suffer is if it doesn't look as though you are. If you run into him on the street you don't want his pity, you don't want him to say to himself, 'My God, she looks awful. She must have put on a stone and a half and her eyes have gone squinty. What a mess. I'm sure glad I didn't stay with her.' You want him to say to himself, 'This woman is gorgeous. She's thin, her skin is clear, her eyes are big and beautiful. She doesn't miss me at all. She's having one hell of a time. Any day now she's going to start this torrid affair with Tom Cruise and I'm going to feel like the biggest jerk since Ike Turner.'

4. Maintain your stress level. Remember the mega-stress diet? A broken heart is stress of the highest order. You're edgy, you're nervous, you're excitable, adrenaline jams your bloodstream like BMWs jam the motorway out of the city on a Friday afternoon. Keep it up. Make a list of all the wrongs he ever did you, of all the mean things he ever said to you, of all the times he let you down, of all the promises he made that he never kept. Whenever you feel yourself settling down to a low stress level, read your list. Whenever you find yourself thinking, I don't feel so bad anymore so I think I'll have breakfast, get out your list and read just one of his misdemeanours out loud. If you still feel like a roll and jam, call someone and

read it to them. As soon as you hear them say, 'You're kidding! Oh my God! He did *that*?' you won't want to eat for the rest of the week.

'You see, Serena,' says Jane. 'Where most people go wrong with their diets is that they think of dieting as passive. You know, don't do this and don't eat that. But there's really nothing to it if you just use your imagination a little.'

Nothing to it? Jane, if there's nothing to it, why have we all been on diets for most of our lives? If there's nothing to it, why is it that at any given time more women are trying to lose weight than are *not* trying to lose it? Who is supporting the billion-pound dieting industry? If it's so easy, why are we all so sensitive about the size of our bums?

'Okay, Serena, okay. So maybe it's not quite *that* easy....'

8.

The Road to the Fridge Is Paved with Good Intentions (or Sticking to Your Diet)

The Gap between Theory and Practice

Deciding that it's time to go on a diet is simple enough. And deciding which diet to go on isn't particularly difficult either. So far so good, you think to yourself. Not bad at all. My bum wobbles when I walk and I'm going to live on plums and diet cola for the next four months, I can handle that. No sweat.

But, of course, as any veteran dieter can tell you, the hard part hasn't yet begun. The hard part doesn't even begin on the day after you've strip-mined the kitchen, on the day your diet actually begins. It waits. It bides its time.

The first days of your diet slip by as easily as a greased pig slips through the hands of the farmer who is trying to catch it. You bounce around looking smug and virtuous, holding up your hand dismissively whenever someone tries to pass you a tea cake or a toasted scone. 'Oh, no,' you say, 'I'm on a diet.'

'I admire you,' they say, spreading their scone with lashings of cholesterol and sugar. 'I can never keep to one for long.'

You note the flabby belly, the chubby arms, the sagging chin. You think of the carrot sticks and cottage cheese of home. You smile. 'It's not just the losing weight,' you say. 'It's the healthier eating as well.' Your smile grows.

A week passes. You stop feeling hungry all the time. You stop dreaming about hot beef sandwiches and Bakewell tarts. The deprivation is almost exhilarating. You couldn't feel more awe, excitement, or accomplishment if you were walking on the moon instead of living on lichees and pickled watermelon rind. Your friends grow weary of hearing you wonder out loud how you could have gone on so long eating fettuccine alfredo and deep-fried mushrooms when you could have been eating raw spinach and brown rice. 'Can you imagine?' you beam. 'When I think of all the time I've wasted....'

Sadly, however, we all know that this euphoric state of high resolve doesn't last. Like the memory of a goldfish, a person's unquestioning love for shredded cabbage is short. In fact, ironically enough, it's usually roughly forty-eight minutes after you've convinced yourself that you could probably live on bean sprouts and steamed fish for the rest of your life that you find yourself standing at the till with a bag of prawn cocktail crisps in your hand. 'Now how did that get there?' you ask yourself. Damned if you know. But since it's already been rung up....

If food were illegal — and therefore both difficult and dangerous to obtain — it might be possible to diet for a month or two without ever contemplating backsliding, without ever giving in to the seductions of a mushroom pizza. But unlike certain controlled substances, food is not illegal. You don't have to sneak into bad neighbourhoods in the dead of night in order to get a box of doughnuts. You don't have to hang out in sleazy bars with gaunt-looking men with bad teeth in order to procure a hot dog and a side order of crinkle-cut chips. You're not going to get arrested because you've got a quarter of wine gums in your pocket or onion rings on your breath.

And, also unlike certain controlled substances, food is all around you every minute of the day — being eaten, being sold, being advertised, being thrust at you from every direction — no matter where you are, or who you are, or how you spend your free time. Is it any wonder, then, that it is easier to give up hard drugs than to give up cream buns and sugar in your tea?

Is it any wonder, then, that the most important contribution that we in the twentieth century have made to civilization — aside from consumer capitalism and the atomic bomb — is the concept of The Binge?

The Binge?

Yes, The Binge.

In previous centuries, people just ate. Sometimes they ate a lot. Breakfast, lunch, dinner, tea, a little late supper after the theatre or during the battle. If they were really hungry, or especially greedy, they'd have second helpings and maybe even thirds. One gets the impression, in fact, that people used to quite like food. They enjoyed it. They revelled in it. Having food was generally a good sign. If someone came to visit you and found the table sagging under a weight of cakes and pies and small roasted animals they wouldn't say, 'Jesus, Pandora, pigging out again?', but 'Wow, this is great! You must be doing well!' And, likewise, nowhere in the lore and literature of the first nineteen centuries or so of Western Civilization will you encounter that phenomenon known as The Binge. The Ancient World had its orgies, of course, but they were to The Binge what a squad of SAS gunmen are to a chimp with an Uzi.

'Uh, Serena?' you say. 'I know this is going to sound kind of stupid, but I'm very young and I've never been on a diet and I was raised in the Orkneys by people with a very high metabolic rate, so could you tell me exactly what you mean when you say "binge"?'

Quicker than Jane in a bad mood can get through a box of shortbread and a jar of Nutella.

A Simple Fable for Our Times

The Monster That Ate the Kitchen

A Short Horror Story

It is a dark, stormy night. Outside, the trees are tossed about by an angry wind; the rain claws at the glass; lightning tears the sky. It is a night of danger and treachery. A night when evil spirits sprint behind the clouds and dreadful monsters, woken from their ancient slumbers, once more stir and lumber 'cross the land. It is a night to stay locked in your room, a crucifix clutched in your hand, a prayer on your lips. A night to stay safely indoors where the creatures of blackness can't reach you and mark you as their own. But on a night like this, is 'safe' a word that has any meaning? On a night like this, would the Holy Grail itself be enough to protect you from the demons of hell?

Shhhh....

The house is still. The kitchen is quiet. But what is that? A slight sound in the hallway? A creaking on the stairs? Something wild and lonely cries in the night. Something whimpers in the storm. And then, faintly at first, they hear it. They think they hear it. Stealthy steps on the stairs. Something tip-toeing through the hall. The quiet of the kitchen becomes a hush.

There is a rustle of tiny voices, no louder than a breath.

'What is that?'

'Did you hear something?'

'You don't think ...?'

Thunder stills them. The room is illuminated in a sudden explosion of lightning. Everyone huddles close together, quaking with terror, peering out from their hiding places, ceasing to breathe.

'Is it?'

'Could it ...?'

'Do you ...?'

But there is nothing there — only darkness and the screamings of the night.

'It's all right,' the voices sigh. 'There's no one there.'

'It was just the wind.'

'It was something outside.'

'We're just feeling jumpy.'

But then, silently — silently and oh-so-slowly — the doorknob turns.

'What's that?'

A sixteenth of an inch.

'Is someone there?'

An eighth.

'Can you see something?'

A quarter.

'Who is it?'

A half.

Another hand grenade of lightning flares through the room. Slowly, slowly, and without a sound, the door opens a crack. There are gasps and hisses and infinitesimal squeals. Small hearts pound.

'Oh no!'

'It can't be!'

'Oh, please, God. Not this! Anything but this!'

They hold on to one another. They close their eyes. They try to hide more deeply in the shadows.

But there is no place to go. Nowhere to hide. No way out.

'What shall we do?' they whisper urgently to one another. 'Oh, dear Lord, what shall we do?'

The door to the kitchen opens fully. The light goes on. There, wildeyed and terrible to see, long white teeth gleaming in a blood-red mouth, it stands, breathing heavily, aquiver with unnatural desires. 'Food!' it shrieks, like a desperate cry from the bowels of hell. 'Food! I must have food!'

The bag of apricots in the drawer starts to tremble. There is a rumble from the fridge. In the fruit bowl, the apples and satsumas begin to weep. The box of cornflakes in the pantry chatters. The jar of pickled onions faints.

'She's coming!' scream the savoury biscuits. 'She's coming!'

'She's after me!' wails the box of treacle tarts! 'Oh, just look at the look in her eye! She's after me! She's after me! Oh please, save me, save me, don't let me go like this!'

'And what about us?' moans the six-pack of crisps. 'What about us? In less than two minutes, we'll all be empty packets, balled up in the bin.'

'Shut up, the lot of you!' order the peanuts. 'How can you whinge and bicker at a time like this? We're none of us safe when the mood's upon her, and you know it. Not even the capers or the stale digestives are safe. Not even those green cherries left over from Christmas. Not even that quarter of a jar of honey that's gone all white on top.'

A thin, high voice is heard from the back of the larder. 'What! Not even the rusks two years over their expiry date?'

'Not even you,' say the peanuts solemnly. 'No one. No thing.'

'Oh, but surely we're all right,' call the frozen peas. 'Surely we're safe enough.'

There's a hollow laugh from the vegetable crisper. 'That's what you think! But this is no ordinary person. This is someone who would finish off the mango chutney with the sprouting potatoes. This is no ordinary hunger. This is a hunger that would consume the three bendy carrots left in the fridge with half a bottle of ketchup.'

There are several strangled sobs from the shelf where the tinned goods and jars clink and clank against one another. 'Oh, no!' gasps the tuna. 'You don't mean . . .?' groans the tomato soup. The fancy fruit salad screams, 'Help! Help!'

The cupboard doors are flung wide. The drawers are pulled out. The fridge is wrenched open. 'Yes!' roar the peanuts, trying to duck behind a jar of kidney beans. An enormous, grasping hand reaches out and drags the peanuts into the light. The room freezes as the sound of cellophane being ripped open with fiendish pleasure drowns out the sound of the howling storm. 'Yes!' scream the peanuts, their voices shrill and shaking, growing fainter as the first terrifying crunches are heard, turning to moans of pain as a few nuts are carelessly but savagely scattered to the floor. 'Yes! It is she from whom no one is safe. It's the monster that devoured the kitchen! The Binge has begun!'

This Isn't a Break from Your Diet, This Is the Road to Hell

'Even the ketchup and the stale digestives?' you ask in a mixture of awe and disbelief.

Even the capers and that one dill pickle that's been sitting in its jar like a lab specimen since 1988.

'Wow,' you say, 'that's really frightening.'

It's what we professional social observers call a societal calling card. Like foot-binding or throwing out children you don't want to keep.

'But what differentiates The Binge from the eating you do on the day before your diet starts?'

Jane?

'Oh, really, Serena, this is so obvious. Two totally distinct patterns of behaviour are in force here. In the case of the latter, you *have* to eat everything in the house. That stands to reason. If you don't eat it, it'll be there to tempt you tomorrow. And also, if you don't eat it all you won't have enough guilt and self-disgust to get you through the first few days. You might feel so at peace with yourself on the day your diet begins that you allow yourself an extra crisp-bread or a little bit of marmalade on your dry toast. This, of course, is the thin edge of the wedge. So, you see, it's important for your psychological state *and* your resolve that you clear out the kitchen before you begin. The Binge, however, is completely different. Serena?'

The Binge can come at any time, day or night, summer or winter, whether you're happy or depressed, and whether you're on a diet or not. One minute you're walking to the car, your arms filled with beauty aids and a new off-the-shoulder blue sweater, and the next you're ducked down in the back seat, eating a dozen doughnuts, one right after the other, only pausing long enough to get some air into your lungs now and then. When The Binge happens when you're on a diet, however, it is not just an embarrassing episode that you don't like to talk about. You can't just dust the sugar from your fingers and toss the box under someone else's jeep and forget about it. It isn't something that can be dismissed by carrying the rubbish to someone else's bin at the other end of the street and sweeping up all the crumbs. It can't just be covered up by saying that you had to throw everything out because the freezer mysteriously decided to self-defrost. Twelve Bounty bars during the course of a normal day is, perhaps, a little extreme. But twelve Bounty bars during the course of a dieting day is worse than bad news.

'How much worse?'

A lot. Because if it's a normal day, and you've had a normal breakfast, and a normal lunch, and a pleasant supper, and then, for some reason as difficult to understand as quantum mechanics, you come up with the idea that twelve Bounty bars would round the day off nicely, you'll probably stop there. You are going to feel a little unwell afterwards and will probably skip that cup of cocoa at bedtime. And the next day you may take your coffee black and miss out on the biscuit you usually have with your morning tea. But it is unlikely that, having wolfed down twelve chocolate-covered bars of coconut and white death, you are then going to finish off the jar of peanut butter with a spoon. It's not inconceivable, of course, but it is unlikely that you are going to eat every grain of cereal in the house, even that intended for the baby's breakfast, from the box, while standing at the sink, pretending to do the dishes.

But when a dieter binges, a dieter binges in style. The stories of what a dieting binger will eat, and in what proportions, and in what space of time, would make Stephen King cringe. 'Saints preserve us!' Stephen King would exclaim. 'What's a ghoul or a vampire next to a woman who will eat ten tuna sandwiches at one go and then sneak into her young child's room and eat the giant chocolate egg he's been saving since Easter?'

Once the dieter starts bingeing two things happen.

The first is that the hunger, not to say starvation, that has driven the dieter to this ugly pass is finally acknowledged and out in the open. It's like letting the evil genie out of the lamp he's been trapped in for the past four thousand years and thinking he's going to behave himself. For weeks, maybe even months, the dieter has been sipping her broth and nibbling demurely on her rice cakes and cucumber slices and saying positive things like, 'Hungry? No, actually, I don't feel hungry at all.' There's even been loose talk about never being able to face a sausage hero again as long as she lives. There's been even looser talk about this diet being more effective than the time she was hypnotized, or the time she had her jaw wired, or the time she had acupuncture to help her lose weight. 'I just have no appetite,' she tells anyone who will listen. 'Half an egg salad sandwich and I feel like a beached whale. Really.' And then all of a sudden, late one night while her family slumbers, she finds herself standing in the kitchen with her hand on the Raisin Bran. 'Just a mouthful,' she promises. The box winces. The raisins chatter nervously. The bran flakes rustle. 'One mouthful,' she swears. 'Not one gram more.' But the second that mouthful hits her body her cells all start screaming, 'Food! Food! She's sending down food!' Repressed for so long, the dieter's body, like that sneaky little genie, goes wild. It starts jumping up and down and screaming. There's no stopping it, and little it won't eat. This isn't hunger as we know it, this is binge hunger, far beyond all common restraints of time and space.

The second thing that happens is that even as the dieter's sated cells are beginning to collapse in a state of sheer exhaustion, guilt comes bustling onto the scene. Guilt takes one long look around him at the empty boxes and bags, the apple cores and olive pits and bits of cheese rind, and guilt starts hollering. 'Now you've done it!' guilt roars. 'Now you'll never be beautiful. Now you'll never be skinny. Now no one will ever like you again. Look at that! Just look at it! You've even eaten the All-Bran. Nobody in the history of mankind has ever eaten the All-Bran as well as everything else. Just what sort of a person are you, anyway?' And our poor dieter, whose terror of food was bad enough to begin with, is by now almost beside herself with remorse. Deep in her heart, she knew she should never have taken that first bite. If she could take just one bite she wouldn't be on this stupid diet to begin with. So, while guilt stomps up and down, telling her that Cher never eats more than two tangerines a day, telling her that Jamie Lee Curtis would rather have her teeth pulled out than let so much as one cream puff pass her lips, assuring her that her husband is going to fall in love with someone thin now, or that the cute guy at the garage would never ask out anybody who's plump, like, for instance, her, she thinks to herself: why stop now? She may as well eat everything left in the kitchen. Why not? She has nothing to live for anymore. She might as well go out and eat everything the rest of the world has to offer. London. Paris. Hong Kong. Rochdale, Lancashire.

Fighting Back

'What is it with you, Serena?' asks Jane. 'You always make things sound more difficult than they really are.'

I do?

'Yes, you do. You've just made it sound as though it's impossible to stay on a diet. You've just made it sound as though anyone who tries is doomed to devour half of Yorkshire with no sign of remorse.'

So?

'For the love of lettuce, Serena, a binge is not the end of the world.'

It's definitely the end of some worlds. If you happen to be a cheese cracker or a pickled onion, for example.

'No, it's not. It's like a tornado or a flash flood. It's nature's way of tidying things up. And anyway, not everyone who goes on a diet winds up bingeing.'

Jane, what about the time you were staying with me and you were on the asparagus diet? What about that?

'What about it? I lost five pounds on that diet, though it's true that my urine did turn a peculiar shade of green.'

I also came down to breakfast one morning to discover that you'd eaten every form of carbohydrate in the house.

'I don't believe you're bringing this up again, Serena. You know as well as I do that I was sound asleep at the time.'

Nobody eats marmalade sandwiches in their sleep, Jane.

'If you don't mind, Serena, the point I was trying to make was that there are a lot of sensible ways to stick to your diet and make it work once it's begun. And to diminish remarkably the possibility of a serious or even mega-binge.'

We're all ears.

Dieting Tips from a Pro

1. ***Don't think of yourself as being on a diet; think of yourself as being in a state of civil war***.

What are you saying, Jane, that you're your own worst enemy?

Yes, Jane is saying something like that. She is saying that a diet is no more than the thin half of you (or the half that would be thin) against the fat half of you (or the half that wouldn't bat an eye if you had to wear boiler suits and tent dresses for the rest of your life). If you want the slender you to destroy the troops of fatty tissue and be victorious, Jane says, then you'll have to realize that drastic measures are called for. The war won't be won at the dinner table or the snack counter alone. It won't be won by following the rules of the Geneva Convention. It's a psychological as well as a physical war. A war that eschews conventional weapons and battlefields. We're talking guerrilla tactics here. We're talking of no holds barred, no prisoners taken, no mercy shown.

a. Weigh yourself every day, twice a day. Don't skip a day because you drank too much beer last night or it was your birthday and you ate half the cake.

b. Don't be shy about telling people what you weigh. Humiliate yourself as often as possible. The more you cringe and blush at telling the entire office that you and Danny DeVito are the same height, weight and build, the more determined you'll be to get into shape.

c. Make a graph that charts your progress from the weight you are when you begin your diet to what you consider to be your ideal weight and hang it in the bathroom where you have an unobstructed view of it from your scales.

d. Invest in a full-length mirror and study yourself in it, naked *and* fully dressed, every morning and night. Be tough on yourself. Don't say, 'Not bad,' when you know that there isn't a construction worker in the universe who wouldn't roll his eyes at the sight of your thighs.

e. Wire the fridge. A small stinkbomb is useful for this, but if you're not handy with chemicals a simple alarm system will do. One person Jane knows rigged her fridge so that every time she opens it macabre laughter rings through the kitchen. Another person Jane knows has a tape of herself reciting an original version of 'This Little Piggy' that plays every time she opens the door [This porky little piggy went to market/This pudgy little piggy stayed at home/This bad little piggy ate fattening, artery-hardening roast beef/ This good little piggy ate none/But you, little piggy, scarfed up everything in the fridge and then waddled and cried all the way home]. If you're of a simple nature, an ordinary burglar alarm, the kind that wakes your neighbours in the dead of night and that is difficult to turn off, will do.

f. Tape a picture of yourself in a bathing suit to the door of the fridge and to the door of the pantry. If possible, it's a good idea to tape a picture of a heartstoppingly thin and beautiful model next to the picture of you. It makes more of an impact.

g. If you're on the shy side when it comes to

decorating the house with pictures of yourself half-dressed, you can tape a message to the fridge door instead. WHY ARE YOU OPENING THIS DOOR? is a good one. So are: THINK BEFORE YOU EAT and BUT WILL THIS BE THE LAST TIME? Some dieters find it additionally helpful to affix a sign to the door of the kitchen as well: ABANDON HOPE, ALL WHO ENTER HERE, or IS THIS TRIP REALLY NECESSARY, or CARELESS EATING COSTS LIVES.

h. Train your family to police you. The single dieter has only herself to rely on for will power and control, but the dieter who is part of a supporting family group has endless resources. Small children who will ask in loud, clear voices in public places, 'Mummy, why aren't you skinny and beautiful like Lisa Bazooka's mother?' Smaller children who need no prompting to inform the lady at the till that their mother is on a diet again. Children of a slightly more wordly age who will take the opportunity of a three-hour wait in the doctor's waiting room to ask you if you're going to have a baby like that lady over there. Use them. Encourage them to tell their father when they discover you hitting the chocolate again. Reward them for snooping through the trash for ice cream wrappers and prawn cracker bags. Don't start crying if every time you go to eat something they make oinking noises. Thank them, embrace them, tell them, 'My children, I'm so grateful to you for caring about the size of my inner thighs.' Never go shopping alone. Even the youngest child can learn to spot the unexplained box of cream buns or the unnecessary packet of oat cakes and jar of raspberry jam. The child who can speak in sentences, no matter how simple or lacking in pronouns, can learn to say, 'But, Mummy, you're not supposed to eat barbecued spareribs, are you?'

Men, of course, do not have to be trained to monitor your diet for you. They do it naturally. Even when you're not on a diet they are the first to remark on the size of the piece of cake you've taken or the amount of cheese you've put on your sandwich. You might have told yourself that the cleaners shrank that red dress or that the reason those jeans feel a little snug is because they've just been washed, but the mate of your soul won't be taken in by that. 'Putting on a few pounds, aren't we Pandora?' he'll say. 'Lift you into my arms and carry you into the bedroom?' he'll chortle. 'You must be mad. I'll break my back.' He'll pat your bottom as you're walking up the staircase ahead of him. 'Remember how thin you were when I first met you?' he'll say. One balmy summer evening you'll be strolling arm in arm along the beach. Slender young women with small breasts and no tops to their bathing costumes will be cavorting in the sand. 'Why can't you look like that?' he'll ask you, sighing sadly as his eyes fall on your one-piece suit with the full skirt to discreetly hide the worst of your hips. Some women, bitter, not exactly incredibly thin and stunningly beautiful women who refuse to wear make-up, women like Serena, cite this sort of behaviour as proof that men are insensitive and shallow, but that couldn't be further from the truth. Men behave like that because they know that all women want to be feminine and desirable. And thin. They behave like that because they're trying to help. Don't slap him when he says that he's always considered himself a leg, not a joint, man. Don't burst into tears because his response to your announcement that you're going to go on a diet is, 'When?' Thank him for showing you the error of three meals a day. Applaud him for being interested in your well being. When the day comes that he turns to you and says, 'Darling, all the chaps at work are jealous of me since they saw you in that red catsuit at the Christmas party,' you'll be glad you did.

i. Use aversion techniques to ensure that, even when eating ordinary food, as opposed to dieter's food, you never over-indulge. Put too much salt on your meal, or too much pepper or chilli. Drown your chips in vinegar (and if this has no effect, sprinkle them with sugar instead of salt). Just as you're about to tuck into the moussaka, say to yourself, 'This isn't aubergine, it's large slugs.' Remember what you learned from the restaurant diet and always take very small portions of things you like and very large portions of things that make you want to toss your cookies. Eat on small plates with small utensils. If you're having a special meal that would test the will power of a major prophet — a Chinese banquet or Christmas dinner, for example — wear something a size too small that cuts into your stomach, slows your circulation, makes breathing difficult, and causes your thighs to feel about the size of prize-winning water-melons.

j. Record everything you eat. Yes, everything. There isn't one single dieter anywhere in the universe who hasn't at one time or another said, 'I don't know why I don't lose weight, I never eat anything.' And we believe it. We believe it because it's true. We know how to sit down to a three-course meal and not actually eat a thing. We spend fifteen minutes cutting up the cabbage and another fifteen mashing the potato, and then we move things around on our plates for a while. We take small portions, very small bites, and we chew everything, including the cottage cheese. We never finish anything, not even the salad. Serena refuses to believe this, but it's a proven fact that a really proficient dieter can have more on her plate when the meal's ended than she did when it began. So how come we still can't get into those red jeans? How come the area between our breasts and our thighs looks more like Montana than Nevada? Because we forget about the hundreds of hidden calories that lie in wait for us throughout the day. Because, our mind's on something else, we don't remember to count the butter on that cheese sandwich, or that handful of cereal, or the taste we took of the spaghetti sauce, or the three chips little Robert left on his plate that we ate while we were clearing up. The hidden calorie is the spy in the battle of the bulge. There it lurks, quiet, innocent-looking, doing nothing to bring attention to itself, but all the while sabotaging your diligence and good intentions. So carry a notebook and pen with you at all times. Write down every flake, drop, and morsel that touches your lips. Don't miss one. Count the couple of crisps you sneaked from little Leonie's bag when she went to the loo. Count the bite you took from the baby's rusk. If you licked the icing spoon when you were making your daughter's birthday cake, write it down. Write down every crumb of cake or icing that you picked off the partygoer's plates, every spoonful of jelly and every Smartie, every half a sausage roll and drop of ketchup. And be specific, write down all ingredients. Was the jelly made with water or juice? Was the sausage roll brushed with butter or milk or both? Did the cake contain butter or low-fat margarine? If your husband says, 'Dear, just try this potato soup, it's out of this world,' and you try it, write it down. But don't just write, 'taste of Arnold's potato soup'. Write: potato soup, probable contents: potatoes, onions, butter, flour, milk, seasonings and half a crouton. In this way, and in this way only, can you keep track of what you really do eat. Instead of thinking, well, I did eat a couple of olives, you will know that, in truth, you ate twenty-seven olives, plus herbs. Instead of believing that all you had all day was half a grapefruit, you will know that what you really had was half a grapefruit, three taco chips, one teaspoon of guacamole (avocado, tomato, coriander, lemon juice, chilli, onion), quarter of a slice of toast (one-inch thick wholemeal bread, butter, cream cheese, strawberry jam), two spoons of cornflakes (cornflakes, milk, sugar, a sliver of banana), two pieces of cheddar cheese that fell out of the sandwich you made for your son, one slice of cucumber (ditto) and a daub of pickle (absentmindedly licked from the knife), three tablespoons of chicken noodle soup and a soggy water biscuit (left by the youngest), two good-sized mouthfuls of baked beans (left by the oldest), one Malteser (left in the bag by mistake), a swallow of cola (the oldest), a swallow of orange juice (the middle child), a swallow of chocolate milk (the youngest), half a lemon custard cream (the middle child), roughly one third of an apple (the youngest) and a slice of tomato, lightly touched with mayonnaise, that the middle child picked out of her sandwich. Half a grapefruit? Nothing? Careless eating: The Enemy Within.

2. *Cheat.*

Cheat? Jane, you can't be serious. What's the point of dedicating a lifetime to fighting the side of you that likes nothing more than a good corned beef sandwich and a tub of raspberry ripple ice cream, and then suggesting that the way to win is to cheat? I can't believe that this is what the Viet Cong would have called surprise tactics. I mean, is this really logical? Is this practical? Does this make sense?

Jane says that it does make sense. She says that dieting is not only like a military conflict between peoples who share a common culture and background, it is also like life. In dieting, as in life, says Jane, honesty isn't always the best policy. The end is more important than the means. Sometimes, says Jane, a person needs a little morale boost, a little encouragement to help her get through, even more than she needs to slough off another ounce and a half.

'You know,' says Jane. 'It's sort of like when you're an innocent child and your mother tells you that of course you're going to grow. "Don't you worry, dear," your mother tells you, bending down so you can hear her, "you won't always be called 'Titch'." Well, being on a diet's just like being the shortest kid in your class. The last thing you need to hear when you're the shortest twelve-year-old that ever attended your school is that you're probably a midget and might as well get used to buying your clothes in the pre-teen department because you're going to be buying them there for a long long time. You need to hear your mother say exactly what she does say: that you're not really short, and that even if you were short you're not going to stay like that for ever.'

And just so, Jane maintains, the last thing a person on a diet needs to hear is that she'll never be able to eat chocolate mousse again, or that she's been on breadsticks and water for three weeks and hasn't lost an ounce. She needs to be encouraged, to be pampered, to be treated well.

'That's why it's all right to cheat now and then,' says Jane. 'It keeps your spirits high and allows you to return to diet another day.'

a. Fool your scales. This is almost the first thing any aspiring dieter should learn to do. Lean against the wall when you're weighing yourself, or keep one foot on the floor. Some people like to stand way back on the scales, which works, but is precarious (I once nearly concussed myself using this method). If your scales are talking scales, it's especially uplifting to hear that little android voice say, 'Who is that? Pandora, that isn't you, is it?' If you're afraid someone might walk into the bathroom while you're weighing yourself and find you half-sitting on the clothes hamper, the simplest thing to do, of course, is adjust the scales so that they always read five or ten pounds lighter than they should. This is impossible with talking scales, because they have a tendency to start beeping and screaming, 'Error! Error!' so that the whole house can hear them.

b. Give yourself a treat cheat. So now and then you

sneak a little low-fat margarine on your crisp-bread or dip your rice cake into the peanut butter, so what? So the danger, of course, is that that forbidden biscuit or slice of quiche will be like the alcoholic's one drink — half a glass of cheap wine and the next thing you know you're sitting in a laundry basket in the middle of the road, trying to explain to the arresting officer how you got there and, if possible, why. For this reason, I invented the treat cheat. The treat cheat works on the theory that if you allow yourself the occasional (or even regular) treat, the desire to sit in front of the fridge and impersonate an industrial Hoover will never suddenly overwhelm you.

There are two varieties of the treat cheat. The first works best with calorie-controlled diets. You weigh out everything you eat, just as usual. You measure your slices of boiled chicken and thin toast, just as usual. You drink only water, black tea, coffee and broth, just as usual. But once a day you allow yourself a little something that you aren't supposed to have. Something small but exquisite. Something to bask in and savour. It might be one perfect chocolate cream. It might be one stunning egg custard. It might be half a samosa. A small packet of crisps. A handful of dry-roasted nuts. You can have this treat at any time of the day, but you must eat it slowly and you must *never* eat more than your allotment. You can, however, save it up. For instance, instead of letting yourself have half a cup of raisins every afternoon at four o'clock, you can wait four days and have two cups (or wait four days and have a cheese Danish).

The second variety of treat cheat works with

any sort of diet. It is simple, but effective. You go off your diet once a week. Sunday's a good day to choose, because so little ever happens on a Sunday that few people manage to stay on their diet anyway. In some circles, in fact, Sunday is known as the day when the hills are alive with the sounds of churchbells and fridge doors being opened and closed. So if that's your treat cheat day, you're well ahead of the game. You have the laid-back attitude and confidence of knowing that you didn't sabotage your diet, you were never meant to be on it. Thus, there is no danger that you're going to wake up on Monday morning with a guilt hangover and a burning desire for pancakes. Psychologically, the weekly treat cheat is so brilliant it's almost frightening. For, hate though I do to admit it, Serena is right about one thing; it's the hopelessness, the endlessness of the diet that gets people down. Like sunday afternoon, it stretches Sahara-like before you: it's just there, one bit looks exactly like another, and it goes on for ever. But if every so often you are allowed to flop down on this oasis and stuff your face with dates and almonds, then you automatically have the strength to wade out into the dunes again.

3. *Never eat out.*

Never eat out? Jane, have you lost your mind? I know that you think that no woman who isn't at least fairly attractive and reasonably presentable when put in a pair of leggings will ever be asked out on a date, but even women who don't look like Kelly McGillis have friends and mothers who occasionally ask them to meet them in that Greek place near the barber's shop or invite them over on Saturday for a bowl of soup.

'Eating out for a dieter is like going white-water rafting when you don't know how to swim. There's only a 0.00001 per cent chance that you won't fall in.'

It is true, of course, that one of the biggest challenges any dieter can face is that of going out to eat. It is, in fact, a challenge similar to that faced by the young Native American boy who would be a brave. He must leave his friends and family, put his quiver on his back, strap his knife to his belt, and with only a little dried buffalo meat go off into the wilderness by himself to become a man. She must leave behind her low-fat yoghurt, her scales, her mirrors, her exercise machines, her tape measures, her alarm systems on all food storage units, and the photograph of herself looking like a marshmallow in a white track suit that's taped to the door of the fridge. The young would-be warrior must face the gods of the elements all on his own, must stand up to the spirits of the night and of the future and the past; and the dieter must face a world where people eat and drink as though they have never heard of flab, podge, or thunder thighs, where they don't give a tuppence whether or not the sauce on the chicken was made with skimmed milk or whole, where bowls of nuts and fruit and crisps and twiglets are wantonly left out within anyone's reach. What is the possibility of dropping your knife just as the mountain lion leaps for your throat compared to the reality of peer pressure?

It is no wonder that your average dieter becomes nervous, underconfident, and easily thrown when away from the confines of her own safe home. Her mind addled by the aromas of cooked food, she forgets to order her salad without dressing. Confused by the abundance of carbohydrates and fats, she can't remember the average caloric value of a small prawn. Thrown by the sight of several other perfectly respectable looking people buttering their rolls, she starts buttering hers. It's as though she is a girl again, unable to leave her room because she doesn't have the same white pleated skirt as every other girl in her group. It's as though she's a girl again, stealing bubble-gum from the corner shop because Alison Hayman stole bubble-gum from the corner shop. Only now what she is doing is ordering a starter and knocking back the bread because everybody else is. If the answer, years ago, to the maternal question 'If all the other girls were jumping off a bridge, would you jump off too?' was, 'Yes', then today it is, 'And if all the other girls are eating double helpings of stuffed manicotti and garlic bread instead of water-cress and steamed onions I'm eating them too.'

'That's exactly what I mean,' says Jane.

But Jane, that doesn't mean that you have to stay in your room for the rest of your life. The young Native American has to wrestle the grizzly and come to terms with the ghosts of his ancestors, and the perpetual dieter has to learn how to handle herself among non-dieters and even over-eaters.

'I guess dining in a restaurant now and then is all right,' says Jane, 'as long as you remember the rules:

a. Always try to stick as close to the restaurant diet as you can.

b. If possible, frequent only really bad or mediocre restaurants where you won't be too tempted to eat.

c. You don't have to be polite in a restaurant. In a restaurant, neither good manners nor your mother's habit of becoming hysterical if everyone doesn't eat three helpings of every course is going to pressure you into eating more than your diet will take. Waiters, unlike hostesses and female relatives, are quiet, impersonal and paid to serve, not complain because you don't finish your crêpes.

d. Make sure the restaurant you choose is over-priced (not a difficult thing to do these days), so that you won't want to order very much anyway. (NB: French restaurants specializing in nouvelle cuisine — portions are so small that even someone fasting could eat an entire meal without cheating — and Thai restaurants — healthy food in small servings at prices so high that you feel as though you must have fed half of China when you get the bill — are highly recommended. Avoid Eastern European and good Italian restaurants at all costs.)

e. Don't be embarrassed to ask your waitress to weigh your salad or measure your roll for you. That's what she's paid for.

Eating at the home of another human being, however, says Jane, is something else again. You're no longer limited to one serving and controlled portions. Your appetite can no longer be squashed by simply looking over at the cost of the fried cheese.

'Precisely what I was trying to say before,' says Jane. 'A whale suddenly finding himself at a convention of Japanese fishermen has more chance of a good time, than a dieter invited to the Smiths' dinner party has of surviving the evening without putting on ten pounds.'

Why is this? I foolishly ask.

'I'll tell you why,' says Jane. 'This is because

human beings like to see other people eat. Human beings especially like to see other people eat if they themselves are on a diet. Since, at any given moment, 78 per cent of all the women you are likely to know will be on a diet, and since most dinner invitations are extended by women, most people who invite you over for a meal will be dieting women who want to see everybody else make pigs of themselves while they nibble a lettuce leaf.'

Jane, I think I have to make an interjection here.

'And what would that be, Serena?'

I just think it's a little extreme to suggest that the only reason anyone asks you to supper is because they want to see you eat two helpings of gnocchi with pesto and half a loaf of bread.

'It's the only reason I ever invite anyone over.'

Jane, please, a woman who once talked of having her stomach stapled cannot be considered a model of normal behaviour.

'Well what about my first mother-in-law, Leonora?'

Oh, come on, Jane, Leonora wasn't normal either. She had plastic sheets on all her furniture. You can't expect rational behaviour from someone who covers even her coffee table in cling film.

'Tell them.'

The first time Jane met Leonora was several months after she and Beowulf were married. Leonora didn't give out dinner invitations to just anyone, you see. And, too, she had a very busy life, coming down with migraines and polishing the plastic on the furniture, so it was a while after the nuptials before an appointment could be arranged. As soon as Jane and Beowulf had gingerly seated themselves on the sofa, concentrating hard on not sliding off, Leonora started passing around dishes of nuts and crisps and crackers. 'Help yourself,' Leonora kept urging, 'don't be shy.' 'What's wrong?' Leonora would ask if a daughter-in-law refused another fistful of salted peanuts and another half a pound of cheese and onion crisps. 'I went all over for these, don't you like them?' Jane, assuming that Leonora assumed that she and Beowulf, waiting for this evening, hadn't eaten since the wedding, did her best to oblige her hostess. Also, of course, she didn't want to get off on the wrong foot with the mother of the man who hadn't yet ceased being the love of her life. Then came the meal itself. Leonora filled the plates in the kitchen. 'You should've seen them,' Jane recalls. 'You'd have thought she worked in the zoo or something the way she piled on the chicken casserole.' But when Jane looked over at Leonora she noticed that Leonora's plate contained only one small slice of boiled chicken, two small lettuce leaves, and three slices of cucumber. And then Jane and Beowulf were forced to eat cheese and biscuits ('But you must have some, I went to this special cheese shop twenty miles away for the walnut cheddar') and chocolate custard ('I made it especially') while Leonora nibbled on half a Bath Oliver and a sliver of Stilton. After that there were chocolates. And after that the pastries Leonora had forgotten to put out with the custard.

'By the time we staggered out of there,' says Jane, still bitter even after all these years, 'I felt like I'd consumed the dinner of three African elephants. Which I probably had. While Leonora had taken in exactly 325 calories.' Jane sneers. 'See what I mean?'

Nonetheless, Jane, I don't think your theory offers the most reasonable explanation.

'Okay, Serena, so what's your theory?'

My theory is this. Though they are not themselves encouraged to eat, women are, as we have already discussed, nonetheless seen as society's nurturers and, of course, cooks. Mum's apple pie. Granny's biscuits. Ravioli just like Mama used to make. A man who can't make himself a bowl of rice is endearing. But a woman who can't whip up a dish of macaroni cheese is defective. 'What's the matter with her?' everyone wants to know. 'She can't cook.'

If you went to Harry's house and he ordered a takeaway, you wouldn't think anything of it. 'Well, Harry's been known to burn water,' you'd say. 'And anyway who cares? He's a brilliant cellist and he knows more elephant jokes than anyone this side of the Atlantic.' But go to Mary's and be given a carton of chicken vindaloo and a stuffed paratha from the Star of Delhi and the tune changes slightly. 'I don't care if she's just got back from that important United Nations conference on children's rights, you'd think she could pop a soufflé in the oven, wouldn't you?' you grumble. 'An omelette at the very least,' agree the other guests.

And if, when your mother went to Palestine to research a book she was writing, your father fed his children on pizza from the place around the corner and hamburgers from a fast-food chain, you wouldn't have complained, would you? Of course not. Years later, you wouldn't have told your therapist, 'My God, you should have seen his idea of scrambled eggs! It's no wonder I'm so neurotic.' You would have thought your dad was great, letting you have all the chips and ham and pineapple pizza a child might want. And, too, the neighbours — the women neighbours — would have invited you all over to supper now and then or brought by pots of soup and nutritious casseroles, but they would never have said that they thought your father wasn't doing his job. It's your mother they'd have blamed. 'Imagine her going off like that and not worrying about feeding those adorable children.' But if your father had gone off to Palestine to research her book for her, leaving your mother, as at home in the kitchen as a sea bass is in a cornfield, in charge of meals, then everyone would have been scandalized. 'She can't even cook!' the neighbours would whisper. 'Can your imagine? She feeds them on pizza and fish and chips. Those poor little mites!' And, years later, your therapist would really have gotten an earful. '. . . and if you think that's bad, at Christmas, when all the other children had homemade mince pies and a turkey dinner and Christmas pudding, my mother would take us to the Wimpy and let us order anything we wanted,' you'd weep. 'Is it any wonder I've got such deep-seated emotional problems?'

Nor have women missed this message. That's why they like to see other people eat. Because if their guests or children don't eat themselves stupid it can only mean one of three equally disastrous things:

1. Their guests or children did not like the dinner. They didn't like the dinner, not because stuffed cabbage simply isn't something they go a bundle for, but because the person who made the stuffed cabbage is one of the worst cooks the world has ever seen. Because the person who cooked the dinner is a woman (and probably a mother) and should, therefore, be a wonderful cook whose meals make people feel happy, well-fed, cared-for and loved, the guests or children not only think that the stuffed cabbage tasted like old boots, they also think that the person who made the stuffed cabbage is a total failure as a human being.

2. Their guests or children are probably relatively indifferent to the stuffed cabbage. What they don't like is the person who made it.

3. Both. They hated the bloody stuffed cabbage exactly as much as they hate you.

This, I believe, and not the desire to see every other woman in the world wearing baggy jeans with elastic waistbands, is why people who invite you to dinner like to see you eat and be seen to enjoy yourself. It also explains why even the most stubborn dieter can find it difficult to leave her potatoes untasted or refuse to try the rhubarb crumble. Because we know what it's like to be on the other end of the dinner party. To be the person who lay awake for five whole nights, trying to decide what to make; who changed the menu fifteen times; who drove the butcher insane with her demands about the beef; who burnt the first dessert and dumped the original starter on the floor and then cried so much she nearly cancelled the whole damned meal; who before anyone has managed to put a forkful in his or her mouth is already asking, 'How is it? Is it all right?'; who then repeats through the entirety of the meal, 'Is it all right? Are you sure? You're not just saying that are you? Doesn't anyone want a little more?' We all know what it feels like to cook for seven hours and then find yourself with a table of guests who are all on a diet and won't eat anything but the salad.

'Serena, please, you're breaking my heart.'

I'm just trying to put things in some sort of perspective, that's all.

And so, of course, is Jane. Jane says that's all very well and good, but the fact remains that a person on a diet, though she naturally does not want to hurt her hostess's feelings (unless the hostess is her mother, in which case it doesn't matter), also does not want to eat the potatoes or try the rhubarb crumble. So a few points should be kept in mind:

a. Remember, no one ever eats as much in public as they will eat in private. That is just a fact. Therefore, unless your hostess is my mother or Serena, both of whom cook as though they're expecting the All Blacks to drop by, she's probably not going to give you very large portions. Accept gratefully and with profuse thanks, and then eat half.

b. Tell your hostess how delicious everything is several times. She'll be so pleased that she won't be bothered by the fact that you don't actually eat any of it.

c. If your hostess is the type who does get bothered that you barely touch your food — or if she is your mother — bring along a small container or a plastic bag that you can conceal on your lap, and slip as much of your dinner into that as you can.

d. If your hostess has a dog, slip your dinner into him.

e. If your hostess has placed you beside her so that it is a little difficult to slip your dinner into anything besides yourself, the minute she sets the main course on the table you should exclaim, 'Oh, I can't believe this! I forgot to tell you I'm allergic to aubergine stuffed with lamb!'

'Well,' says Jane, 'I guess that pretty much wraps it up, huh, Serena?'

Not quite.

'You think we've left something out?'

I know we have.

'But what? We've covered the whys of diets, and types of diets, and how to keep on a diet, and all the benefits to be derived from being on a diet for over fifteen years. What else is there?'

Everything that you like is fattening.
'What are you talking about now?' sighs Jane.
'Everything you like *is* fattening.'
Read on....

9.

Great Dieting Myths

Dieters make up one of the largest subcultures in the history of mankind. But, unlike most such groups, this is a subculture that crosses all normal boundaries of nation, race and language, rather in the way that being a billionaire businessman or a mercenary does.

Let's say, for instance, that you come from Glasgow. You go to Singapore on holiday. There aren't many Glaswegians in Singapore. There is no haggis. No decent bitter. They don't serve their curried prawns with chips. Despite the nice weather and the lovely scenery, you begin to feel lonely and disheartened. You dream of the cold and the rain. Of dirty brown buildings and stagnant rivers. 'Ach, well,' you cry, 'if only some drunken football supporter in a tartan cap would come along and vomit on my shoes. Then I'd feel better.' Should you actually come across another Glaswegian, even if he or she is precisely the sort of person you would normally most loathe, even if she or he does, in fact, vomit on your shoes, you fall upon each other like long-lost cousins.

But now let's say, to continue the for-instance, that you come from Glasgow and you're on a diet. You go to Singapore on holiday. Singapore is a small and very well-organized country, but one with a limited number of cultural attractions (a zoo, a botanical garden, sand and water). What it does have, however, is great food. Everywhere you go. In other countries people may spend some of their time bowling or fox hunting or doing the crossword, but Singaporeans eat. So not only are you lonely and longing to hear the low lament of a bagpipe, you are going crazy trying to keep your calorie intake under 4,000 a day (holiday or no holiday, you do feel that some restraint should be shown). And then you find yourself, yet again, sitting in a restaurant, eating. Boy, do you wish you'd never left home. You finish your meal (which is incredibly delicious) and the waiter comes over to ask if you'd like some dessert. 'Oh, no,' you say, hastily, 'no thank you.' 'Are you sure?' smiles the waiter. 'We have fresh fruit, ice creams and yoghurts. We have chocolate gateau. We have exquisite pastries made with....' Having already had two meals and three snacks today (for want of anything else to do), and desperate to hang on to what little of your will power remains, you suddenly blurt out, 'I can't. I can't. I'm on a diet.' A hush falls over the restaurant. For the first time since you arrived, people are looking at you not as though you're a tall white tourist looking for a good deal on a camera, but as though you're a human being. The waiter pats your shoulder kindly. 'Well, why didn't you say so?' he asks. 'I've been on a diet for the last six years myself. And my wife, my wife's been on a diet for twelve.' The woman at the next table leans over. 'I'm on a diet too,' she says in a conspiratorial whisper. 'It's murder isn't it?' The next thing you know, you are sitting at a table with seventeen Singaporeans, all of them comparing dieting notes with you and wondering if it's easier to lose weight in Glasgow, where the food is so bad. You have a wonderful time. You talk, you joke, you smile. You tell them how you once threw the scales out the bathroom window in a fit of pique. 'But did you open the window first?' asks one of your new friends, and the others all nudge each other and roar with knowing laughter. You all go out in the evening. They invite you into their homes. When you get back to Scotland everyone wants to know what the people in Singapore were like. 'They're just like us,' you tell them.

'Surely dieting is more like a club than a culture,' butts in Jane.

No, Jane, I think you're mistaken. A culture has its own language, its own code of behaviour, its own support industries. And so do dieters. You can go anywhere in the world and talk about liposuction or cheese and onion crisp addiction and other dieters will know exactly what you mean. A dieter in Swansea and a dieter in Milan both know that no one who is even slightly overweight is ever seen to eat bread and butter or pudding in public. Dieters are one of the most stable and constant consumer markets in the galaxy.

'So are goldfish owners.'

Yes, but a culture, unlike any forty or fifty thousand goldfish owners you care to bring together, has its own mythology. Some of a culture's myths express its fears, some express its hopes, and some reflect its aspirations. But all of them serve as a unifying force. And all of them aren't true. Atlas did not carry the earth on his shoulders, St George did not slay the dragon, and Spider Woman did not create the twins.

'Exactly where is this leading, Serena?' asks Jane.

The Greeks, the Christians and the Hopi are not alone in their mythologizing. Dieters have their myths too.

'Don't tell me. You mean like Everything You Like Is Fattening?'

Got it in one.

Everything You Like Is Fattening

This is the sort of myth — like the ones about the world being flat and that there are dragons in the forest — that is guaranteed to keep people in a constant state of terror. Oh, no, I better not go out too far, they say to themselves, I'll fall off the edge. Oh, no, I better not go into the woods, I'll be burnt to a crisp by a creature with buggy eyes and pointy ears. Better keep away from anything that tastes good or I'll look like a blimp.

'Yes, but Serena, dear,' says Jane. 'As I already tried to point out, it is not a myth that everything you like is fattening. It's a fact.'

Not exactly. If you can disengage yourself emotionally from ginger-nut creams for a second and think about it seriously, you will see that the psychology of this myth is extremely clever and even snide. For by believing that only the things that are fattening are really and truly wonderful, and really and truly loved by you, it gives them an importance in your life that they would never otherwise have.

For example. You're all on your own one dull Saturday night, you finished that great novel you were reading and there's nothing on television that wouldn't put a hyperactive three-year-old to sleep. You feel a little peckish. I know, you say to yourself, I'll have a little snack and listen to some Randy Newman. That should perk me up. And instantly, instead of thinking of apples or a bit of cheese or some delicious pistachio nuts, you think of chocolate-toffee-crunch ice cream. Because you were born liking chocolate-toffee-crunch ice cream more than goat's cheese and almonds? Or because you are descended from people who were kicked out of the Garden of Eden for doing the one thing they were told not to do? 'Don't eat the apple,' said God. And wham-bang, faster than a crazed binger can devour a bag of crisps, there they were, biting into the apple. 'Stay away from the chocolate-toffee-crunch ice cream,' everyone tells you. And wham-bang, there you are heading out to the late-night shop with a wild look in your eyes. In the end what happens is that you start liking things just because they are fattening. 'Ooh, it's got cream, chocolate, butter *and* three tons of sugar in it, it *must* be good!' And not liking things because they aren't. 'What, nothing that will clog my arteries? Nothing that will rot my teeth? Nothing that will make my face break out? This can't be very good.'

The other point, of course, is that a lot of the things you like aren't fattening. Pasta. Rice. The humble but brilliant baked potato. The glorious apple. The carrot and the pumpkin, the chick pea and the dried apricot. But because they are not forbidden they have no glamour, they have no allure. We forget we like them. We think we just eat them so we have something to do between desserts.

Fat Girls Never Have Any Fun

The fat girl myth is as basic to human civilization as the creation myth. And, like the creation myth, has as many variants as the forest has leaves. We can trace it back to that perennial favourite, the All Princesses Have To Be Beautiful myth, made popular several hundred years ago by grumpy male fairy tale writers — itself an extension of the No One Ever Thumps An Unattractive Cave Woman Over the Head, Ugly Women Are Witches, and There's No Such Thing As An Obese Nymph With Bad Skin myths. In all of these myths, the heroines are always extremely gorgeous, and any woman who isn't extremely gorgeous is either wicked, stupid, or not worth mentioning. Ugliness is equated with evil, nastiness or spinsterhood; beauty with goodness, happiness, and dancing late into the night.

But the concept of beauty, of course, changes with fashion. So as time passed, and beauty began to shed those pounds, and princesses and dancing girls became a little thin on the ground, the Fat Girls Never Have Any Fun myth was created. This one says that fat girls never have any dates, never have sex, never laugh, never have a good time, never get married, and never know any personal fulfilment or joy. You can tell this is a myth, because if you reverse it it is saying that the only people who ever go out, ever have sex, ever laugh, ever have a good time, ever get married, and ever know any personal fulfilment or happiness are all thin. And, by extension, that if you are thin and pretty you won't have any problems. You can only believe this if you never go out. You can only believe this if you think being Cybil Shepherd is more fun than being Bette Midler. You can only believe this if you have a tendency to confuse life with a Coca-Cola commercial.

Another popular contemporary version of this is the Only Pretty Girls Ever Find Love myth.

'Oh come on, Serena,' grumbles Jane, 'do you think Warren Beatty would go out with someone who looked like your Aunt Beryl? Do you think George Michael dates girls who look like Roseanne Barr?'

Funnily enough, I wasn't thinking of Warren Beatty or George Michael at all. But I was thinking of my Aunt Beryl. Aunt Beryl and Marilyn Monroe. Marilyn Monroe, unlike my Aunt Beryl, was pretty by anybody's standards. She was not super slim, but, unlike my Aunt Beryl — a woman who resembles nothing so much as a large postbox or a small mountain — she had a good figure. My Aunt Beryl could walk naked through the Bull and Crumpet on a Saturday night with a rose in her teeth without drawing anyone's attention from the darts game or the argument over Newcastle Brown Ale versus Grolsch, but Marilyn Monroe couldn't walk through the market in a boiler suit with a bag over her head without causing a riot. Norman Mailer, who knows a lot about women, has written several books about Marilyn Monroe, but the only mention my Aunt Beryl has ever had in print has been from me, and none too favourable at that.

But was Marilyn Monroe happy? Did Marilyn Monroe, goddess of the twentieth century, ever find love? No, she did not. And what about my Aunt Beryl? One of the happiest women the planet has ever hosted. My Aunt Beryl met my Uncle Bert in a crowded lift two days before Christmas in 1956. She dropped the kettle she had bought for her mother on his foot and he handed it back to her. It was love at first sight. They repaired to the tea bar to eat a few dozen scones with cream and jam, and to determine the damage done to Bert's foot and my Aunt Beryl's kettle. They were married on Valentine's Day, 1957, the bride looking a bit like the Matterhorn in white crêpe de Chine. My Aunt Beryl and Uncle Bert are one of those rare couples that give marriage a good name, and though it is of course never spoken of, everyone in the family knows that Aunt Beryl and Uncle Bert have a sex life that would be the envy of a rabbit. He can't keep his hands off her, and vice versa.

'And you think that proves your point that a person can be chubby and have puffy cheeks and still find love.'

Of course I do.

'Yes, Serena, but the fact still remains....'

I know exactly what Jane's about to say. Thus taking us to our next myth....

It Is Better to Be Skinny and Unhappy Than Fat and Unhappy

Only if you figure that if you're skinny and unhappy there are a lot of chocolate doughnuts and rum-raisin ice cream between you and being fat and unhappy and, therefore, a few bonus moments of joy. Other than that, you're probably a lot better off being fat and unhappy than skinny and unhappy, because if you're fat and unhappy, things being what they are, you're probably unhappy because you're fat, and if worse comes to worse you can always sew your lips shut and change your life. But if you're skinny and unhappy — and skinny is the most desirable state this world seems to have to offer, next to stupendously wealthy or a close friend of Bruce Springsteen — well, then there's nowhere to go, is there?

A companion myth to this is the It Is Better To Be Skinny and Unhappy Than Fat and *Happy* myth. Jane argues that anyone who is fat and happy is under some sort of terrible delusion. 'After all,' argues Jane, 'what could a person with the body of a dumpling have to be happy about? How can you be happy when you know that when you walk into a room men don't immediately start undressing you with their eyes?'

Now there's a tricky one. How about being alive? Sunsets? Sunrises? Doing a worthwhile job well? Being able to listen to Mozart whenever you want? Baby elephants? Having *Tootsie* on videotape for those nights when you need a good laugh?

Jane sighs. 'I'm sorry Serena,' says Jane, 'but I just don't think that anybody who has hips, a bum, a tummy, or the slightest sign of thighs could possibly be happy.'

And I don't see how anybody who has starved herself down to a size eight and then, for the rest of her life, has to live in the constant fear of putting it all back on, could be happy.

'She could be,' says Jane.

Then what about myth number four?

Happiness Makes You Fat

'Oh, don't start,' says Jane.

I first heard this myth in 1980, when I was briefly in love with a fiddle player named Leon. I heard it from Jane. 'You better watch your step, Serena,' Jane warned me, 'or you're going to get a big bum again.'

I put a dollop of taramasalata on my cracker and replied that I thought she'd always told me that love made you skinny.

'That's only unrequited or feckless love,' answered Jane. 'That's why I always fall for jerks and bastards and men who are in love with someone else. You get to have the thrill of being in love with none of the surplus weight. Happiness, though. Happiness is a killer.'

The myth goes something like this. If you are unhappy, you lose your appetite. Uninterested in living to any significant degree, you are also un-interested in doing anything that might contribute to living (like eating) or that might cheer you up or excite your senses (also like eating). When a person is happy, however, she forgets to pay attention to her calorie intake. She feels impervious, superhuman, beyond the dangers of cream soups and candied yams. Instead of locking herself into the bathroom when she feels hungry, and repeating the lifetime dieter's chant ('Better famished than fat, better famished than fat, better famished than fat'), she skips lightly to the fridge and starts fixing herself a triple decker sandwich. She hums to herself as she pours on the Russian dressing. She dances across the kitchen with the jar of sauerkraut in her hand, singing 'Zip-A-Dee-Doo-Dah'. She puts on enough cheese to make sure the Swiss economy is healthy for the next ten years. Where a person less careless about her diet would take one bite and then quickly throw the rest away, on top of the old dog food and under a pile of coffee grounds, she wolfs down the whole thing.

Considering the fact that the companion myth to Happiness Makes You Fat is Depression Makes You Fat, it's hard to know what a person's supposed to do. The truth is that some people chuck out their calorie counters when they're happy and don't gain an ounce because the adrenaline of joy is zapping through their bloodstream, and some people use being happy as an excuse to finish off the treacle pudding; and that some people lose their appetite when they're depressed, and others use it as an excuse to finish off the treacle pudding.

There Are Certain Days And Seasons When Your Diet Doesn't Count

Everybody believes this one. Even I believed this one.

Scene: it is a quiet afternoon. Your children are in the living room, watching some video involving gun-toting psychopaths. You wander into the living room to see how many of the original characters are still alive. Your oldest child looks up. 'Mum,' says your oldest child, 'what's that in your hand?' You look down as though you may have forgotten. 'It's an ice cream,' you say. Your oldest child, who always was a little precocious and takes after her father's side of the family, stares into your eyes rather coolly. 'I thought you were on a diet,' she says. You stare back, cool as well. 'It's Sunday,' you say.

Sundays, national holidays, birthdays, anniversaries, the day you take the cat to be done, the day you win the jingle competition, the day you lose your wallet, keys and the tiny square of cloth you once managed to rip from Barry Manilow's shirt, holidays even if they're only to sit in a chalet in Cornwall and watch it rain for a week; all of these are times when a diet doesn't count.

'Well,' you say, 'that makes sense. You yourself said you can't diet forever. And you certainly wouldn't want to be eating crispbread on a Caribbean cruise when everyone else is stuffing themselves with crab baked in banana leaves and getting smashed on Piña Coladas, would you?'

I couldn't agree with you more. But what you're overlooking here are the operative words 'doesn't count'. It isn't that you are going off your diet because it's Sunday and it's either eat a meal or scrub out the loo. It's that you can eat whatever you want and it's not going to affect your diet. It's like being given the shield that makes you invisible. 'Oh,' says your fairy godmother, 'it's Prince Philip's birthday tomorrow. In that case, don't give another thought to going out for a pizza after work. You can eat as much as you want, it'll be just as though you haven't consumed a thing.'

Watching Other People Eat A Lot Is the Same As Dieting

The lifetime dieter, whose life, as we have seen, is built to a large degree on superstition and fable, frequently believes that someone else eating is exactly the same as she herself not eating. So if you are out to lunch with a dieter and you order the strawberry cheesecake for dessert, she feels slim. If you have had the fried brie for a starter and the fettuccine for your main course and then have the strawberry cheesecake, she will not only feel slim, she will feel as though she's lost weight.

The same thing happens if several friends are having dinner together. After a delightful meal of vegetarian lasagne, the hostess asks if anyone is interested in the apple pie that she's prepared for dessert. Now, imagine that all of you are on a diet. 'Oh, no thanks, Pan,' you say, 'I'm really full.' 'Me too,' say the other guests. 'I know what you mean,' sighs Pandora, 'that lasagne is really filling, isn't it?' You all make the face of a person with the appetite of a bird who has eaten a dinosaur. And, indeed, that's how you feel. Even though you all know that as soon as the front door shuts behind you Pandora will either eat half the apple pie standing up or will chuck the whole thing down the loo, and even though you all do feel virtuous, you have snarfled down a lot of lasagne noodles layered with beans and cheese and are sure you're going to pay for it by discovering in the morning that you've put on twelve ounces and your chin's broken out. But imagine that though you say, 'Oh, no, Pandora, darling, I couldn't eat another mouthful,' and though Constance Jackson says, 'Oh, gosh, Panny, I couldn't even breathe near it, I've eaten so much,' Pandora and Audrey (either in the grips of massive depressions or beside themselves with transcendental joy) both opt for dessert. They have enormous wedges of pie, covered with cream. Audrey has seconds. Then how do you feel? You feel as though you've lost a stone, that's how you feel. You forget the three slabs of lasagne, the olive bread and the blue cheese dressing on the salad. You forget the thirty-seven olives you ate while you were waiting for Pandora to serve dinner. You feel great. Every spoonful of apple pie and cream that Audrey and your hostess shovel into their mouths represents 5,000 calories trimmed off your body weight. By the time you're ready to leave you feel slimmer than you did after the three weeks you spent on the lentil and water diet in 1988.

Using this logic, perhaps the answer isn't to be on a perpetual diet. Perhaps the answer is to move in with a family of heavy-weight boxers.

It Doesn't Count If You Don't Enjoy It

Sister to the It Doesn't Count If You Break It In Half myth, the concept that if you're not really enjoying what you're eating — that if you spend the half-hour it takes you to polish off the steak and Stilton pie moaning and groaning and repeating over and over, 'I hate this, I hate myself, Oh my God I'm going to be as big as a hotel' — your body somehow won't notice the extra 4,022 calories you've just put into it, is one of the greatest (and least mentioned) of all the dieting myths.

'Oh, I get it,' you say. 'It's like thinking that if you cross your fingers before you lie to someone you're not really lying.'

Sort of. Only it's more insidious. Because at its heart is the idea that you're not meant to enjoy your food. That eating is wrong. That it's okay to do it as long as it makes you suffer, but not if it gives you pleasure. So, as long as every mouthful of the apple pie is causing you agony and heartbreak, even if your body does notice you have paid for your transgression, it's all right.

10.

Famous Last Words

'Famous last words? You mean like, "never again"?'

Not exactly.

'You mean like "only just one"?'

Uh uh.

'"This is the last"? "I'll never eat again as long as I live"? "From now on I'm sticking to tangerines"? "Tomorrow"? "As soon as I finish this"? "I'll pay for this later"? "Just a tiny tiny slice"? "Just a taste"?'

Actually, the famous last words I had in mind come from Marlon Brando. Interviewed at the beginning of 1990 on a BBC chat show, Mr Brando had this to say about his crash diet:

'Stay out of bed, and stay active,
and eat rice and fish — and eventually you die.'

I couldn't have put it better myself.

BEACHED ON THE SHORES OF LOVE

Serena Gray

'A single woman over thirty-five has more chance of being shot by a terrorist than of finding a man'
Newsweek

You are an intelligent, attractive, sophisticated and independent woman. You have a good job, a terrific flat, a fantastic record collection, hundreds of interesting, exciting friends, great legs, holidays in the Himalayas and a leather mini-skirt. You don't need men. You can open your own jars, fix your own car, and leave your own socks on the floor. You, survivor of more than one relationship that has put both your stamina and your sense of humour to the test, can do very nicely on your own, thank you very much. Let others join dating clubs and singles groups. And yet, every now and then, you sometimes hear yourself say things like, 'I really hate champagne dinners for one.' Still find yourself wondering if the man who signs himself Lonely in Luton in the personals might be half as good as he sounds. Still secretly root for Cinderella. Still think that, someday, your prince is going to come.

BEACHED ON THE SHORES OF LOVE
The hilarious cure for the post-feminist blues

FUTURA PUBLICATIONS
NON FICTION
0 7088 4322 0

AVAILABLE LIGHT

Ellen Currie

'Kitty, a fashion stylist . . . wakes up one morning to find that her lover Rambeau, a gambler, has left her. As the couple's paths separate, the rich and compelling story widens too, stretching familiar patterns of love into amazing events . . . This is a tall tale told in vibrant prose, with high good humour and respect for unshared but universal secrets . . . Ellen Currie nudges reality and uncovers a vein of the fabulous . . . as if Fra Angelico's "Annunciation" has been retouched by Salvador Dali and used as a backdrop for a rock video . . .'
The New York Times Book Review

'This slightly surreal, mildly manic, often sad and unusually funny first novel by Ellen Currie is about natural children and unnatural parents; guilt and pain, and loss passed along, like blue eyes or brown hair, from generation to generation . . . Currie's antic vision is sharp; her gentle wit has bite; her extravagances ring true. Best of all is her delicious prose. When Currie turns a phrase she sends it spinning . . .'
San Francisco Chronicle

'An astounding first novel . . . a pungent, ferociously funny tale'
Walter Clemons, *Newsweek*

'Its language and wit will make you laugh out loud. A book about generations, guilt, and the maddening drive for the ownership of babies'
Grace Paley

FUTURA PUBLICATIONS
FICTION
0 7088 3921 5

TOPSY DINGO WILD DOG

Camilla Carr

'A strenuous laff-riot first novel featuring rural West Texas eccentrics, grotesques, hoopla geriatric sex, and funeral-parlour follies.'
Kirkus Reviews

TOPSY DINGO WILD DOG is the hilarious and occasionally bizarre tale of Mary Jane Shady as she comes home to Uncertain, Texas, for her twentieth-year high school reunion. Mary Jane went to Hollywood to become a Legend; she returns instead as 'Miss Peanut Butter Cup', star of a series of TV commercials.

But hot in pursuit of Mary Jane are her obnoxious Los Angeles agent and New York film crew, complete with the black and beautiful Arabella du Noir. And when the big city sophisticates collide with the West Texas natives, the result is a riotous culture clash *extraordinaire*.

For Uncertain is a town like no other, teeming with eccentrics: only there would Mary Jane find Baby Flowers, a vague but extraordinary beauty who aimlessly walks the streets shedding her clothes, and Siamese twins running for Homecoming Queen. Or, for that matter, a girl called Topsy Dingo Wild Dog . . .

'TOPSY DINGO WILD DOG is mad and moving, fast and frolicking. Ms Carr has a passionate and original mind and a wild heart that burns with the truth.'
BETH HENLEY, Pulitzer Prize-winning playwright

FUTURA PUBLICATIONS
FICTION
0 7088 4757 9

GIRL TALK

Cindy Blake

LADIES WHO LUNCH TOGETHER . . .

What do three sparkling, sexy, successful career women talk about in smart restaurants? Men – what else. Who needs them? Sam, Georgia and Eugenie do – that's who. Clinking glasses of champagne, they toast their pact to role reversal, for they plan to outplay men at their own game. Now they will seduce the seducers.

THE HUNTRESS . . .

Samantha, gorgeous but unbelievably naive, is tutored by the worldly Georgia and Eugenie in seduction techniques. When they have taught her all they know (and they know an awful lot) she is set loose upon an unsuspecting male victim.

THE PREY . . .

Is *homme fatal*, devastatingly handsome gynaecologist John Rankin. As proficient at putting on charm as he is at taking off bras, he is Sam's prime target. But when faced with such a smooth operator, it is inevitable that the huntress will become the hunted. And the hunt becomes more and more intense, until a sizzling climax is reached in St Lucia, where tangled relationships and steamy passions explode in the hot Caribbean sun.

GIRL TALK

One of the wittiest and most perceptive novels for the nineties.

FUTURA PUBLICATIONS
FICTION
0 7088 4356 5

All Futura Books are available at your bookshop or
newsagent, or can be ordered from the following address:
Futura Books, Cash Sales Department,
P.O. Box 11, Falmouth, Cornwall TR10 9EN.

Please send cheque or postal order (no currency), and
allow 60p for postage and packing for the first book
plus 25p for the second book and 15p for each additional
book ordered up to a maximum charge of £1.90 in U.K.

B.F.P.O. customers please allow 60p for
the first book, 25p for the second book plus 15p per
copy for the next 7 books, thereafter 9p per book

Overseas customers, including Eire, please allow £1.25
for postage and packing for the first book, 75p for the
second book and 28p for each subsequent title ordered.

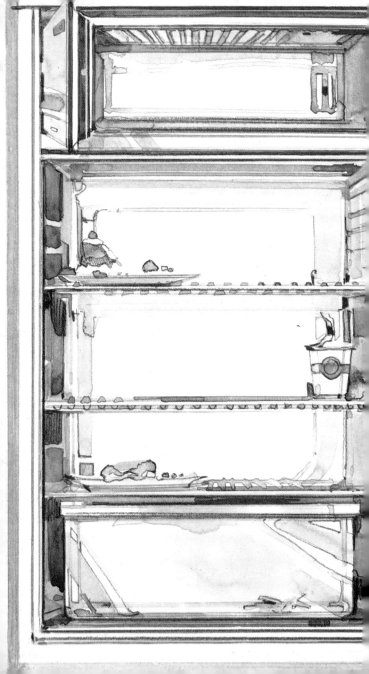